ANALYSIS AND SYNTHESIS OF
LINEAR TIME-VARIABLE SYSTEMS

SCIENCE SURVEYS

(*General Editor:* Edwin F. Beckenbach, Professor of Mathematics, University of California, Los Angeles)

SCIENCE SURVEYS: 1

Analysis and Synthesis of Linear Time-Variable Systems

BY ALLEN R. STUBBERUD

UNIVERSITY OF CALIFORNIA PRESS

BERKELEY AND LOS ANGELES

1964

UNIVERSITY OF CALIFORNIA PRESS
BERKELEY AND LOS ANGELES, CALIFORNIA
CAMBRIDGE UNIVERSITY PRESS
LONDON, ENGLAND
© 1964 BY THE REGENTS OF THE UNIVERSITY OF CALIFORNIA
LIBRARY OF CONGRESS CATALOG CARD NUMBER: 64-20996
PRINTED IN THE UNITED STATES OF AMERICA
DESIGNED BY WARD RITCHIE

PREFACE

The material in this monograph is based on a dissertation of the same title that was submitted in partial fulfillment of the requirements for a Ph.D. in engineering at the University of California, Los Angeles. The research was supported in part by grant AFOSR 62–68, contract AF 33(651)-7154.

This monograph is an attempt to present a complete synthesis technique for linear time-variable systems, an area of research that has not been receiving sufficient attention in recent years. The analysis problem is treated briefly in chapter 3. The reader is assumed to have a knowledge of the fundamental properties of linear ordinary differential equations.

I wish to thank Professor C. T. Leondes of UCLA for his advice and encouragement while this work was being done, Dr. E. B. Stear with whom I worked on the material in chapter 3, and finally my wife, May, for her help and understanding.

A. R. S.

Los Angeles, April, 1964

CONTENTS

Chapter 1

INTRODUCTION

The analysis and synthesis of linear time-invariant systems have, to a great extent, dominated the efforts of engineers in all fields. As a result, a large body of literature on these subjects presently exists at the expense of linear time-variable and nonlinear systems. The reason for this domination stems, first, from the fact that general techniques for the analysis, and consequently the synthesis, of linear time-invariant systems are relatively simple compared to those for linear time-variable and nonlinear systems. Secondly, many linear time-variable and nonlinear systems can be adequately approximated (in some sense) by a linear time-invariant system.

The purpose of this monograph is to partially fill some of the voids in the areas of analysis and synthesis of linear time-variable systems. In particular, the results are slanted toward the field of feedback control systems; they are not, however, limited to this area. The problem of analysis is considered in some detail (chap. 3), but the primary concern is with the problem of synthesis.

It might be added that the techniques and ideas have been developed in enough detail that they are valuable from a practical standpoint. Many of the problems that are most likely to be encountered in a practical design situation have been examined. As a result, a large class of linear time-variable systems can be synthesized by means of the techniques developed in this monograph.

DEFINING THE SYSTEM

Any process that produces a response (output) when an excitation (input) is applied to it, can be called a system (the term transmittance is also used). A system may be depicted as a block as in figure 1.1 where W represents the system,

1

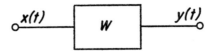

Figure 1.1. A general system.

$x(t)$ represents the input, $y(t)$ the output, and t is the independent variable. If, in addition, the system W is linear, then it must satisfy the following definition:

DEFINITION.

If 1. *an input x_1 produces an output y_1,*
2. *an input x_2 produces an output y_2, and*
3. *an input $c_1 x_1 + c_2 x_2$ produces an output $c_1 y_1 + c_2 y_2$, where x_1, x_2, y_1, and y_2 are arbitrary functions of t and c_1 and c_2 are arbitrary constants, then W is a linear system.*

The definition includes a wide variety of systems, for example, distributed-parameter, lumped-parameter, constant-coefficient, and variable-coefficient. This monograph is limited to the investigation of the class of linear systems that can be described by an ordinary linear differential equation of the form

$$\sum_{i=0}^{n} a_i(t) \frac{d^i y}{dt^i} = \sum_{i=0}^{n} b_i(t) \frac{d^i x}{dt^i}, \qquad \tau \leq t < +\infty,$$

$$\left. \frac{d^i y}{dt^i} \right|_{t=\tau} = 0, \qquad i = 0, 1, 2, \cdots, n-1,$$

(1.1)

where the independent variable t is time, τ is the time of application of the input, the $a_i(t)$ and $b_i(t)$ are continuous and deterministic functions of time, $y(t)$ is the output of the system, and $x(t)$ is the input. In addition, $a_n(t)$ is assumed to be unity (without loss of generality), and any or all of the $b_i(t)$ may be zero in a particular case. This requires that the order of the operator (the upper limit on the summation)

$$\sum_{i=0}^{n} a_i(t) \frac{d^i}{dt^i}$$

is always equal to, or greater than, the order of the operator

$$\sum_{i=0}^{n} b_i(t) \frac{d^i}{dt^i}.$$

In a physical system this means that there are no net differentiations between the input and the output, which is a valid constraint from a physical standpoint (see chap. 4). In the following text, the operator

$$\sum_{i=0}^{n} a_i(t) \frac{d^i}{dt^i}$$

will be referred to as the integral operator of equation (1.1), since it indicates that an integral operation must be performed on the input to generate the output. Similarly, the operator

$$\sum_{i=0}^{n} b_i(t) \frac{d^i}{dt^i}$$

will be referred to as the differential operator, since it indicates that a differential operation is performed on the input in the system.

Another method of defining the types of systems investigated in this monograph is by means of their weighting functions. A linear differential equation of the form in equation (1.1) has associated with it a weighting function (unit impulse response function) $W(t, \tau)$ of the form (refs. [3], [16], [21])

$$W(t, \tau) = \sum_{j=1}^{n} \beta_j(\tau) q_j(t) + b_n(t)\delta(t - \tau), \qquad t \geq \tau, \tag{1.2}$$

$$= 0, \qquad t < \tau,$$

where $\delta(t - \tau)$ is the Dirac delta function, the $q_i(t)$ are linearly independent solutions of the homogeneous portion of equation (1.1), that is,

$$\sum_{i=0}^{n} a_i(t) \frac{d_i q_j}{dt^i} = 0, \quad j = 1, 2, \cdots, n, \tag{1.3}$$

and the $\beta_j(\tau)$ are given by

$$\beta_j(\tau) = \sum_{i=0}^{n} (-1)^i \frac{d^i}{d\tau^i} [b_i(\tau)\alpha_j(\tau)], \tag{1.4}$$

in which the $\alpha_i(\tau)$ are determined from the set of simultaneous equations

$$\alpha_1(\tau) q_1(\tau) + \cdots + \alpha_n(\tau) q_n(\tau) = 0,$$

$$\alpha_1(\tau) \frac{dq_1(\tau)}{d\tau} + \cdots + \alpha_n(\tau) \frac{dq_n(\tau)}{d\tau} = 0,$$

$$\cdots \cdots \cdots \cdots \cdots \cdots \cdots \tag{1.5}$$

$$\alpha_1(\tau) \frac{d^{n-1}q_1(\tau)}{d\tau^{n-1}} + \cdots + \alpha_n(\tau) \frac{d^{n-1}q_n(\tau)}{d\tau^{n-1}} = 1.$$

The condition that $W(t, \tau)$ be zero for $t < \tau$ guarantees that the system is physically realizable. The equivalence of a weighting function of the form in equation (1.2) with a differential equation of the form in (1.1) is discussed in Appendix I. It is shown that, subject to the necessity of an adequate number of derivatives of the $\beta_j(\tau)$ and $q_i(t)$, a differential equation of the form in equation (1.1) can be generated from a weighting function of the form in equation (1.2). Because of this equivalence, either equation (1.1) or (1.2) may be used to define a particular system.

PREVIOUS WORK

The previous work in the analysis and synthesis of linear time-variable systems in engineering applications may be conveniently classified according to the mathematical representations, called transfer functions, used to describe the systems. Evaluation of this work must depend a great deal upon the various properties of these mathematical representations.

In evaluating the representations, three important criteria are these:
1. How difficult is it to arrive at the representation?
2. How much information about the system response is *readily* available from each representation?
3. How difficult are the operations of combining (cascade and parallel combinations, etc.) and manipulating systems when they are described by the representation?

The three most general types of transfer functions are the following:
1. Weighting functions.
2. Time-variable frequency response functions.
3. Differential equations.

Techniques for generating integral transforms for general linear time-variable differential equations have also been developed [1], [14]; however, these techniques have proved to be too specialized or too difficult for use in a general theory that includes both analysis and synthesis.

Weighting Functions (refs. [3], [5], [13], [15], [18], [20], [21], [30])

The weighting function has long been used as a tool in the analysis of linear systems. Its value lies in the fact that knowledge of the weighting function allows the response of a system to be determined for any input by means of the convolution integral; that is, if $W(t, \tau)$ is the weighting function of a linear system, then for an input $x(t)$ the output $y(t)$ is given by

$$y(t) = \int_{-\infty}^{t} W(t, \tau) x(\tau) \, d\tau. \tag{1.6}$$

Thus from the standpoint of criterion (2), the weighting function is an excellent method of representation.

Problems associated with the weighting function are that it is very difficult to determine for a given general linear time-variable differential equation, and that usually it is not expressible in a closed form. In both analysis and synthesis these difficulties may rule out the weighting function as a useful representation. Actually, the amount of difficulty associated with determining a weighting function depends upon the form of the differential equation.

To answer criterion (3), the three critical operations of combination of systems will be examined. These operations are the following:

1. Parallel combination of systems.
2. Cascade combination of systems.
3. Finding an inverse system.

A parallel combination of systems is illustrated in figure 1.2. Let the system W_1 have the weighting function $W_1(t, \tau)$ and the system W_2 have

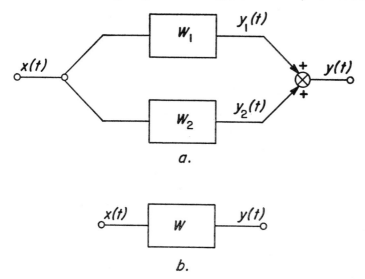

a.

b.

Figure 1.2. Parallel combination of systems.

the weighting function $W_2(t, \tau)$; then

$$y_1(t) = \int_{-\infty}^{t} W_1(t, \tau)x(\tau)d\tau,$$

$$y_2(t) = \int_{-\infty}^{t} W_2(t, \tau)x(\tau)\,d\tau, \tag{1.7}$$

and

$$y(t) = y_1(t) + y_2(t) = \int_{-\infty}^{t} [W_1(t, \tau) + W_2(t, \tau)]x(\tau) \, d\tau.$$

Then the system W in figure 1.2, b, which is equivalent to figure 1.2, a, has a weighting function $W(t, \tau)$ given by

$$W(t, \tau) = W_1(t, \tau) + W_2(t, \tau). \qquad (1.8)$$

Obviously if $y(t) = y_1(t) - y_2(t)$ then the equivalent system has the weighting function

$$W(t, \tau) = W_1(t, \tau) - W_2(t, \tau). \qquad (1.9)$$

A cascade combination of systems is illustrated in figure 1.3. Again

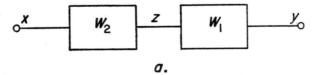

a.

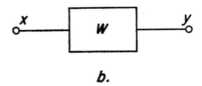

b.

Figure 1.3. Cascade combination of systems.

let W_1 have the weighting function $W_1(t, \tau)$, and let W_2 have the weighting function $W_2(t, \tau)$. **Then**

$$y(t) = \int_{-\infty}^{t} W_1(t, \theta)z(\theta) \, d\theta,$$

$$z(t) = \int_{-\infty}^{t} W_2(t, \tau)x(\tau) \, d\tau; \qquad (1.10)$$

combining these equations,

$$y(t) = \int_{-\infty}^{t} d\theta W_1(t, \theta) \int_{-\infty}^{\theta} W_2(\theta, \tau)x(\tau) \, d\tau$$

$$= \int_{-\infty}^{t} d\tau \, x(\tau) \int_{\tau}^{t} W_1(t, \theta)W_2(\theta, \tau) d\theta. \qquad (1.11)$$

The equivalent system W (fig. 1.3, b) then has the weighting function

$$W(t, \tau) = \int_{\tau}^{t} W_1(t, \theta)W_2(\theta, \tau)d\theta. \qquad (1.12)$$

The final necessary operation, the finding of an inverse system, is illustrated in figure 1.4. Two systems are inverse to each other if, when

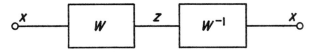

Figure 1.4. Inverse systems.

$x(t)$ is applied as an input to the cascade combination of these systems, the output is also $x(t)$. The system equivalent to this cascade combination evidently has as its weighting function a Dirac delta function. This is apparent from the convolution integral

$$y(t) = \int_{-\infty}^{t} \delta(t - \tau)x(\tau)\, d\tau = x(t). \qquad (1.13)$$

Then by virtue of equation (1.12) the weighting function of the inverse system, $W^{-1}(t, \tau)$, is the solution of the integral equation

$$\delta(t - \tau) = \int_{\tau}^{t} W^{-1}(t, \theta)W(\theta, \tau)\, d\theta, \qquad (1.14)$$

in which $W(t, \tau)$ is the weighting function of W.

The three necessary operations for combining systems represented by weighting functions are then defined by equations (1.8), (1.12), and (1.14). The first two operations are simple and straightforward, but the third—the finding of an inverse—is generally difficult. In addition, the solution may be in the form of an infinite series, which will prove to be too unwieldy to manipulate in the synthesis problem, and the solution must therefore be approximated, usually by truncating the series.

Mal'chikov [18] and Gladkov [13] have examined the problem of synthesizing a given time-variable weighting function as a feedback system using modified versions of these techniques of combination. The disadvantage of their scheme is the requirement that an integral equation must always be solved. Cruz and Van Valkenberg [8], by synthesizing linear time-variable systems in an open-loop configuration, do not encounter the problem of finding inverses.

Time-Variable Frequency Response Functions

The concept of the time-variable frequency function representation of a linear time-variable system was introduced by Zadeh [27], [28], [29]. Because of its close relationship to the system weighting function, its properties are, from the standpoint of the three criteria above, equivalent to those of the weighting function.

The time-variable frequency response function, which is denoted $H(j\omega, t)$, is related to the weighting function by the pair of integrals [30]:

$$H(j\omega, t) = \int_{-\infty}^{\infty} W(t, \tau)e^{-j\omega(t-\tau)} d\tau, \tag{1.15}$$

$$W(t, \tau) = \frac{1}{2\pi} \int_{-\infty}^{\infty} H(j\omega, t)e^{j\omega(t-\tau)} d\omega. \tag{1.16}$$

Equation (1.15) may be considered the definition of $H(j\omega, t)$.

The amount of work involved in determining $H(j\omega, t)$ from a differential equation is equal to that necessary for determining $W(t, \tau)$. The output $y(t)$ of the system for a particular input $x(t)$ can be determined from the integral

$$y(t) = \frac{1}{2\pi} \int_{-\infty}^{\infty} H(j\omega, t)X(j\omega)e^{j\omega t} d\omega, \tag{1.17}$$

where $X(j\omega)$ is the Fourier transform of $x(t)$. Apparently $H(j\omega, t)$ contains as much readily available information as the weighting function and, in general, more than the differential equation.

The techniques for combining time-variable frequency response functions can be obtained immediately by applying the definition in (1.15) to equations (1.8), (1.12), and (1.14). For combining $H_1(j\omega, t)$ and $H_2(j\omega, t)$ in parallel, equation (1.8) becomes

$$H(j\omega, t) = H_1(j\omega, t) + H_2(j\omega, t). \tag{1.18}$$

For combining $H_1(j\omega, t)$ and $H_2(j\omega, t)$ in cascade, equation (1.12) becomes

$$H(j\omega, t) = \frac{1}{2\pi} \int_{-\infty}^{\infty} H_1(j\omega + j\omega', t)e^{j\omega't}$$
$$\cdot \left\{ \int_{-\infty}^{\infty} H_2(j\omega, \theta)e^{-j\omega'\theta} d\theta \right\} d\omega'. \tag{1.19}$$

Finally, the inverse of $H(j\omega, t)$ can be determined by solving the integral equation

$$1 = \frac{1}{2\pi} \int_{-\infty}^{\infty} H^{-1}(j\omega + j\omega', t)e^{j\omega' t}$$

$$\cdot \left\{ \int_{-\infty}^{\infty} H(j\omega, \theta)e^{-j\omega'\theta} d\theta \right\} d\omega', \tag{1.20}$$

which is the equivalent of equation (1.14). Obviously the same difficulty encountered in determining inverses for weighting functions is present in determining inverses for time-variable frequency response functions.

Engineers have found little use for the time-variable frequency response function beyond the analysis of some linear time-variable electrical networks. They have done almost nothing with it in the area of synthesis of systems, since in the choosing of an overall response function the correlation between the system output and the response function is not readily apparent, as it is, for instance, in the case of weighting functions.

Differential Equations

Differential equations are the most common form of representation for a physical system, for the reason that physical laws (such as Ohm's law and Newton's law) when applied to a particular system produce as governing equations, differential equations. To determine the response of the system, these equations must then be solved. Obtaining the solution of a general linear time-variable differential equation is difficult; therefore, a differential equation generally contains less readily available information about system response than a weighting function or time-variable frequency response function. From the standpoint of the first two criteria above, differential equations rate high with respect to the first and low with respect to the second.

The techniques for combining differential equations are developed in chapter 2. With respect to the third criterion, it will be seen that differential equations rate very high. Previous work in the area of techniques for combining differential equations is limited to a few papers by Darlington [9]–[11], in which he briefly mentions that such techniques might be used, but he neither develops nor makes use of them.

In this discussion some of the advantages and disadvantages of the three general representations of linear time-variable systems have been discussed. The discussion is not to imply that one representation should be used to the exclusion of the others. By judicious use of all three, if they are readily available, there may be a great saving in time in analyzing and synthesizing such systems.

Scope of the Monograph

The purpose of this monograph is to develop a general technique for analyzing and, in particular, for synthesizing linear time-variable systems. The emphasis is on techniques for synthesizing feedback control systems, although the techniques need not be confined to these systems.

The first step in the development is the discussion, in chapter 2, of an algebra of differential equations that allows for the combination of differential equations in a manner not unlike the combination of matrices. In chapter 3 the algebra is applied to the analysis of linear systems via signal flow graph theory. In chapter 4 the algebra is applied to the problem of synthesizing given weighting functions (or differential equations) as feedback systems. Chapter 5 is devoted to the producing of overall system functions. In chapter 6 a criterion for determining the reducibility of a linear system is developed along with a technique for reducing the order of a reducible system. Finally, in chapter 7, techniques for approximating given differential equations are developed. The monograph thus provides a complete technique for sythesizing linear time-variable systems and provides, to a lesser degree, techniques for the analysis of these systems.

Chapter 2

AN OPERATOR ALGEBRA FOR DIFFERENTIAL EQUATIONS

In chapter 1 three representations of linear transmittances were discussed along with the advantages and disadvantages of each. It was there stated that the main advantages of the differential equation representation are the relative ease of manipulation and the straightforward techniques of the combining of differential equations.

In this chapter the techniques for combining and the rules of manipulation of differential equations are developed in the form of an algebra of linear transformations.

THE NECESSARY OPERATIONS

Since a linear differential equation of the form

$$\sum_{i=0}^{n} a_i(t) \frac{d^i y}{dt^i} = \sum_{j=0}^{n} b_j(t) \frac{d^j x}{dt^j} \tag{2.1}$$

is a linear transformation of x into y, the algebra is an algebra of linear transformations [2]. The transformations (linear differential equations) that are considered will all have the form of equation (2.1), where some of the $a_i(t)$ and $b_j(t)$ may be zero. In the following development, capital letters $(A, B, C, \cdots)$ are used to represent differential equations of the form of equation (2.1). In addition, all initial conditions are assumed to be zero.

The algebra of differential equations involves three operations:

1. Addition of two differential equations; that is,

$$A + B = C. \tag{2.2}$$

2. Multiplication of a differential equation by a scalar; that is,

$$A p(t) = B, \tag{2.3}$$

11

or

$$p(t)A = C. \tag{2.4}$$

(Clearly, if $p(t)$ is a constant, $B = C$.)

3. Multiplication of two differential equations; that is,

$$BA = C. \tag{2.5}$$

These operations are indicated in block-diagram form in figure 2.1. Obviously, in order for the algebra to be useful, each of the operations must be defined. In addition, the following useful properties of the algebra will be defined:

1. A unity element.
2. A zero element.
3. An additive inverse.
4. A multiplicative inverse.

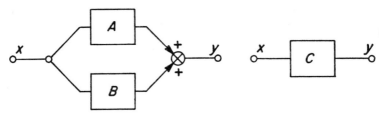

a. ADDITION OF TWO DIFFERENTIAL EQUATIONS

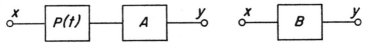

b. POSTMULTIPLICATION OF A DIFFERENTIAL EQUATION BY A SCALAR

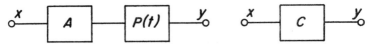

c. PREMULTIPLICATION OF A DIFFERENTIAL EQUATION BY A SCALAR

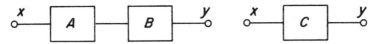

d. MULTIPLICATION OF TWO DIFFERENTIAL EQUATIONS

Figure 2.1. Operations of transformation algebra.

Multiplication of Two Differential Equations

It is necessary to define multiplication first since it is used in defining addition.

Any differential equation of the form in equation (2.1) can be divided into two parts—a differential operator and an integral operator (fig. 2.2).

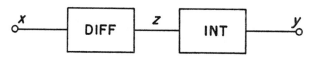

Figure 2.2. Block diagram of differential equation
in terms of the notation of equation (2.1).

The relationships between the variables x, y, and z are, in terms of the notation of equation (2.1),

$$z = \sum_{j=0}^{n} b_j(t) \frac{d^j x}{dt^j}, \tag{2.6}$$

$$\sum_{i=0}^{n} a_i(t) \frac{d^i y}{dt^i} = z. \tag{2.7}$$

The multiplication of two differential equations can be represented by figure 2.3, *a*. The equations that define the relationships between the

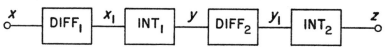

a. PRODUCT OF TWO DIFFERENTIAL EQUATIONS

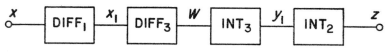

b. EQUIVALENT BLOCK DIAGRAM OF (*a*)

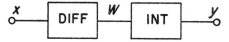

c. EQUIVALENT BLOCK DIAGRAM OF (*b*)

Figure 2.3. Multiplication of two differential equations.

variables in this system are

$$\sum_{j=0}^{n} b_j(t) \frac{d^j x}{dt^j} = x_1 = \sum_{i=0}^{n} a_i(t) \frac{d^i y}{dt^i}, \tag{2.8}$$

$$\sum_{s=0}^{m} f_s(t) \frac{d^s y}{dt^s} = y_1 = \sum_{k=0}^{m} c_k(t) \frac{d^k z}{dt^k}. \tag{2.9}$$

In figure 2.3, b, the two inner operators in figure 2.3, a, have been "interchanged." In general these operators are not commutable; therefore

$$\text{Diff}_2 \neq \text{Diff}_3,$$

$$\text{Int}_1 \neq \text{Int}_3.$$

It is necessary at this point to determine the relationships between x_1, w, and y_1 in terms of the parameters of equations (2.8) and (2.9). Assume that these relationships can be written

$$\sum_{r=0}^{m} g_r(t) \frac{d^r x_1}{dt^r} = w \tag{2.10}$$

and

$$\sum_{s=0}^{n} h_s(t) \frac{d^s y_1}{dt^s} = w, \tag{2.11}$$

where $g_r(t)$ and $h_s(t)$ are as yet unknown coefficients. Substituting the values for x_1 and y_1, each in terms of y, into equations (2.10) and (2.11) produces the relationship

$$\sum_{\alpha=0}^{m} \sum_{i=0}^{n} \sum_{c=0}^{\alpha} \binom{\alpha}{c} g_\alpha(t) \frac{d^{\alpha-c} a_i(t)}{dt^{\alpha-c}} \frac{d^{i+c} y}{dt^{i+c}}$$

$$= \sum_{\beta=0}^{n} \sum_{l=0}^{m} \sum_{\delta=0}^{\beta} \binom{\beta}{\delta} h_\beta(t) \frac{d^{\beta-\delta} f_l(t)}{dt^{\beta-\delta}} \frac{d^{l+\delta} y}{dt^{l+\delta}}, \tag{2.12}$$

where ( ) denotes the binomial coefficient.

If the coefficients of like derivatives of y are equated, a system of $m + n + 1$ simultaneous equations in the $m + n + 2$ unknown $g_\alpha(t)$ and $h_\beta(t)$ is formed. Arbitrarily choosing $h_n(t) = 1$ (without loss of generality) allows these equations to be solved for the remaining $m + n + 1$ unknowns. This operation shows the equivalence of figure 2.3, a, and 2.3, b. Figure 2.3, b, can be further reduced to figure 2.3, c, by combining the differential and integral operators, and the resulting equation is

$$\sum_{\beta=0}^{n} \sum_{k=0}^{m} \sum_{f=0}^{\beta} \binom{\beta}{f} h_\beta(t) \frac{d^{\beta-f} c_k(t)}{dt^{\beta-f}} \frac{d^{k+f} z}{dt^{k+f}}$$

$$= \sum_{\alpha=0}^{m} \sum_{j=0}^{n} \sum_{r=0}^{\alpha} \binom{\alpha}{r} g_\alpha(t) \frac{d^{\alpha-r} b_j(t)}{dt^{\alpha-r}} \frac{d^{j+r} x}{dt^{j+r}}, \qquad (2.13)$$

where x is the system input and z the output. Multiplication of two differential equations defined by equations (2.8) and (2.9) is then defined by the steps indicated in equations (2.10), (2.11), (2.12), and (2.13) and is denoted symbolically by

$$BA = C, \qquad (2.14)$$

where A corresponds to (2.8), B to (2.9), and C to (2.13).

THE UNITY ELEMENT

The unity element is defined as that element which, when applied to a function, leaves the function unchanged. In the differential-equation algebra, the unity element is any differential equation of the form

$$\sum_{i=0}^{n} a_i(t) \frac{d^i x}{dt^i} = \sum_{i=0}^{n} a_i(t) \frac{d^i y}{dt^i}. \qquad (2.15)$$

This can be seen if the output y is written as

$$y = x + y_1. \qquad (2.16)$$

Substituting equation (2.16) into equation (2.15) produces the equation

$$\sum_{i=0}^{n} a_i(t) \frac{d^i y_1}{dt^i} = 0. \qquad (2.17)$$

Thus y_1 is the unforced response (complementary solution) of equation (2.15), and x is the forced response. Assuming no initial conditions on y, $y_1 = 0$ and $y = x$; therefore, an equation of the form in equation (2.15) satisfies the definition of a unity element.

THE MULTIPLICATIVE INVERSE

A multiplicative inverse is defined as a differential equation (denoted as A^{-1}) with the property that if it is multiplied by the differential equation A, a unity element is produced. Symbolically this is denoted

$$A A^{-1} = I. \qquad (2.18)$$

The differential equation of the multiplicative inverse can be found as follows: Consider the cascade transmittances of figure 2.4, *a*, in which

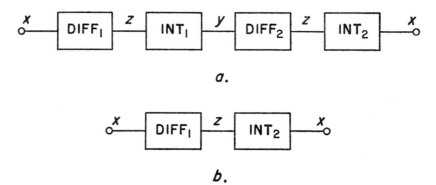

Figure 2.4. Cascade of a transmittance and its inverse.

the transmittances of figure 2.1, d, have been separated into integral and differential operators. The operator Diff_1 has the form

$$\sum_{j=0}^{n} b_j \frac{d^j x}{dt^j} = z, \tag{2.19}$$

and Int_1 has the form

$$z = \sum_{i=0}^{n} a_i \frac{d^i y}{dt^i}. \tag{2.20}$$

If the weighting function corresponding to Int_1 is called $W_1(t, \tau)$, then

$$y(t) = \int_{-\infty}^{t} W_1(t, \tau) z(\tau)\, d\tau, \tag{2.21}$$

where, by the definition of a weighting function,

$$\sum_{i=0}^{n} a_i \frac{\partial^i W_1(t, \tau)}{\partial t^i} = 0. \tag{2.22}$$

Then operating on $y(t)$ with a differential operator of the form

$$\sum_{i=0}^{n} a_i \frac{d^i}{dt^i}$$

produces $z(t)$. This differential operator is the inverse of Int_1.

If Diff_2 is chosen with this differential form, figure 2.4, a, can obviously be reduced to figure 2.4, b. If Int_2 is now given the form

$$z = \sum_{j=0}^{n} b_j \frac{d^j x}{dt^j}, \tag{2.23}$$

figure 2.4, *b*, takes the form of a unity element, as defined by equation (2.15), which is necessary if both input and output are to be *x*. Thus if *A* is represented by the differential equation

$$\sum_{i=0}^{n} a_i(t) \frac{d^i y}{dt^i} = \sum_{j=0}^{n} b_j(t) \frac{d^j x}{dt^j}, \tag{2.24}$$

where *x* is the input and *y* is the output, then A^{-1} is represented by the differential equation

$$\sum_{j=0}^{n} b_j(t) \frac{d^j x}{dt^j} = \sum_{i=0}^{n} a_i(t) \frac{d^i y}{dt^i}, \tag{2.25}$$

where *x* is the output and *y* is the input.

ADDITION OF TWO DIFFERENTIAL EQUATIONS

Addition of two differential equations is represented symbolically in figure 2.5, *a*. As in the case of multiplication, the differential equations have been divided into differential and integral operators. The addition is performed step-by-step as indicated by the block diagrams in figure 2.5, *b–g*.

In step 1 the original system is multiplied by the cascade combination of two differential operators, $(Int_1)^{-1}$ and $[(Int_2)']^{-1}$, and two integral operators, Int_1 and $(Int_2)'$, which are their respective multiplicative inverses. This combination then represents a unity element. Since the system is linear, $(Int_1)^{-1}$ can be moved to the left of the summing junction, thus eliminating Int_1 from the upper element as shown in step 2. Now the integral operator Int_2 and the differential operator $(Int_1)^{-1}$ are multiplied and the product separated into its new differential and integral operators as indicated in step 3, where the new differential operator is denoted $[(Int_1)^{-1}]'$ and the new integral operator is denoted $(Int_2)'$. $(Int_2')^{-1}$ is now moved to the left of the summing junction, thus canceling $(Int_2)'$.

There are now only differential operators to the left of the summing junction and only integral operators to the right. These can be combined as indicated in steps 5 and 6, and addition of differential equations has been defined.

THE ZERO ELEMENT

The zero element in differential-equation algebra is defined as any differential equation whose output is always identically zero. The zero element is denoted 0.

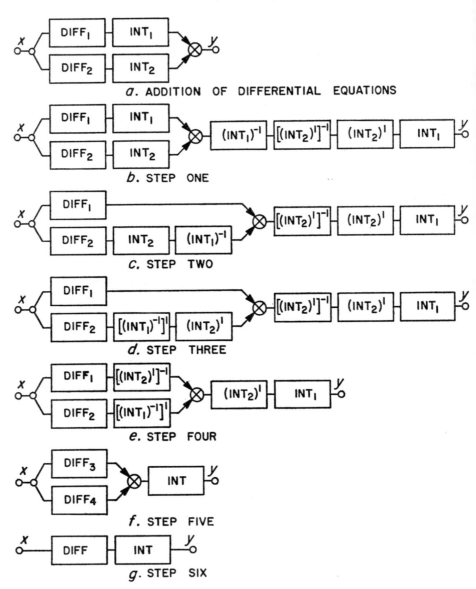

Figure 2.5. Reduction of parallel transmittances.

THE ADDITIVE INVERSE

The additive inverse of a differential equation A is defined as that differential equation B which when added to A produces a zero element; that is,

$$A + B = 0. \tag{2.26}$$

It is obvious that if A is the differential equation

$$\sum_{i=0}^{n} a_i(t) \frac{d^i y}{dt^i} = \sum_{j=0}^{n} b_j(t) \frac{d^j x}{dt^j}, \tag{2.27}$$

where x is the input and y is the output, then B has the form

$$\sum_{i=0}^{n} a_i(t) \frac{d^i y}{dt^i} = - \sum_{j=0}^{n} b_j(t) \frac{d^j x}{dt^j}. \tag{2.28}$$

MULTIPLICATION OF A DIFFERENTIAL EQUATION BY A SCALAR

Multiplication of a differential equation by a scalar can be considered a degenerate case of the multiplication of two differential equations, where one of the differential equations is the degenerate equation

$$y = p(t)x \tag{2.29}$$

in which x is the input and y is the output. The techniques developed for multiplying differential equations are then applicable to multiplication of a differential equation by a scalar.

In addition to the properties of differential equation algebra mentioned above, the following laws hold:
1. Addition is commutative; i.e., $A + B = B + A$.
2. Addition is associative; i.e., $A + (B + C) = (A + B) + C$.
3. Multiplication is not commutative; i.e., $AB \neq BA$. (In the time-invariant case multiplication is commutative.)
4. Multiplication is associative; i.e., $A(BC) = (AB)C$.
5. Distributivity is valid; i.e., $A(B + C) = AB + AC$.

SUMMARY

In this chapter an algebra for differential equations was presented. In the later chapters the algebra will be used to perform the manipulations required in the several methods of analysis and synthesis discussed.

Chapter 3

THE ANALYSIS OF LINEAR TIME-VARIABLE FEEDBACK SYSTEMS VIA SIGNAL-FLOW GRAPH THEORY

Signal-flow graph theory provides the analyst with a method by which a physical system that is described by a set of simultaneous differential and algebraic equations can be analyzed. The information contained in the signal-flow graph is neither more nor less than that contained in the corresponding equations; however, the signal-flow graph provides a visual representation of the system equations from which a logical reduction procedure can be deduced. By this reduction, the system may be put into a form more amenable to analysis.

Linear time-invariant systems are especially well suited to analysis by signal-flow graph techniques, because their properties allow reduction by quite simple computational notions. The equations of the system can be Laplace transformed and, consequently, reduced by elementary algebraic operations. Even if the reduction is done in the time domain, the commutativity of stationary elements and the ease with which time-invariant weighting functions can be determined reduce any computational difficulties to a minimum. Since the Laplace transform is not, in general, useful, nor is the commutativity of elements valid in time-variable systems, the reduction of a time-variable signal-flow graph becomes a quite complex problem, and different reduction techniques are necessary.

In this chapter reduction techniques that are useful in the analysis of time-variable signal-flow graphs are described. These techniques allow the concepts of the essential diagram and the "overall system gain" to be carried over into time-variable systems. From the essential diagram a stability analysis may be carried out, and from the overall system gain equation, a measure of the system sensitivity to parameter changes is possible.

SIGNAL-FLOW GRAPHS—TIME-INVARIANT
VERSUS TIME-VARIABLE

Signal-flow graphs provide the analyst with the same information about a system as do the simultaneous equations describing the system. The advantage of the signal-flow graph lies in the fact that it provides a visual representation of the flow of signals through the system. In addition, inspection of the flow graph allows the analyst to reduce the graph (i.e., eliminate system variables) to a form, or forms, more amenable to analysis of system stability, sensitivity, and other important system characteristics.

Reduction of linear time-invariant signal-flow graphs can be accomplished by elementary arithmetic operations if the system equations are first Laplace transformed. Even if reduction is performed in the time domain, the process is not exceedingly difficult because of the commutativity property of time-invariant elements. Reduction of time-variable signal flow graphs is a much more complex operation, because time-variable equations cannot, in general, be transformed into algebraic equations and because time-variable elements are not commutable. It can be argued that, conceptually, reduction of time-variable flow graphs is no more difficult than reduction of time-invariant flow graphs; however, the actual combinatorial manipulations are much more complex.

The well-known rules for drawing signal-flow graphs of linear time-invariant systems are restated here. The system variables are represented by nodes, and the transmittances W_{kj}, which define the contribution of the node variable x_j to the node variable x_k, are represented by directed branches. Assuming that the system transmittances are represented by their corresponding Laplace transforms, the following rules describe the properties of a time-invariant signal flow graph:

1. Signals travel along branches only in the direction of the arrows.
2. A signal traveling along aey branch is multiplied by the transmittance of that branch.
3. The value of the variable represented by any node is the sum of all signals entering the node.
4. The value of the variable represented by any node is transmitted on all branches leaving that node.

If the transmittances are linear, but time-variable, they can be represented by linear operators, say L_i, where L_i could be a weighting function, a time-variable transfer function, or a differential equation. If the operation which the transmittance performs on an input y is denoted (·), then rule (2) must be modified as follows:

2′. A signal y traveling along any branch is operated upon by the operator L_i that corresponds to that branch, and the resultant output from the branch is $L_i \cdot y$.

THE REDUCTION OF A TIME-VARIABLE SIGNAL-FLOW GRAPH

To illustrate how the differential-equation algebra that was developed in chapter 2 can be applied to the reduction of a signal-flow graph, the techniques of reduction will be applied to a typical signal-flow graph (fig. 3.1, *a*).

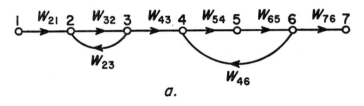

a.

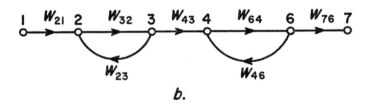

b.

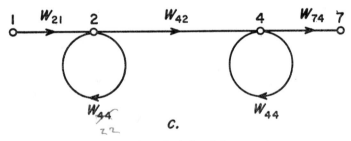

c.

Figure 3.1. A typical signal-flow graph.

Let the transmittances be defined by W_{ij}, where j is the input node of the transmittance and i is the node where the transmittance terminates. In addition, it will be assumed that each transmittance can be defined by an ordinary linear differential equation of the form

$$\sum_{k=0}^{n} a_k(t) \frac{d^k x_i}{dt^k} = \sum_{i=0}^{n} b_i(t) \frac{d^i x_j}{dt^i}, \qquad (3.1)$$

where x_i is the output and x_j is the input. Equation (3.1) can then be written

$$x_i = W_{ij} \cdot x_j. \tag{3.2}$$

The first step in the reduction is to combine the cascade combination of W_{54} and W_{65}, thus forming W_{64} as the differential equation product,

$$W_{64} = W_{65} W_{54}. \tag{3.3}$$

The reduced signal-flow graph is shown in figure 3.1, *b*. This signal-flow graph is in turn reduced to figure 3.1, *c*, by the following combinations:

$$\begin{aligned} W_{44} &= W_{46} W_{64}, \\ W_{22} &= W_{23} W_{32}, \\ W_{74} &= W_{76} W_{64} = W_{76} W_{65} W_{64}, \\ W_{42} &= W_{43} W_{32}. \end{aligned} \tag{3.4}$$

Figure 3.1, *c*, is an essential diagram since it contains only essential nodes [26:100].

The next step in the reduction is to determine the transfer relationship between x_2 and x_1. This is done as follows:

$$x_2 = W_{21} \cdot x_1 + W_{22} \cdot x_2, \tag{3.5}$$

or

$$(I - W_{22}) \cdot x_2 = W_{21} \cdot x_1, \tag{3.6}$$

and

$$x_2 = (I - W_{22})^{-1} W_{21} \cdot x_1. \tag{3.7}$$

Therefore,

$$x_4 = W_{42} \cdot x_2 = W_{42}(I - W_{22})^{-1} W_{21} \cdot x_1; \tag{3.8}$$

but from equations (3.4),

$$x_4 = W_{43} W_{32}(I - W_{23} W_{32})^{-1} W_{21} \cdot x_1, \tag{3.9}$$

and by definition

$$W_{41} = W_{43} W_{32}(I - W_{23} W_{32})^{-1} W_{21}. \tag{3.10}$$

In a similar manner it can be shown that

$$x_7 = W_{74}(I - W_{44})^{-1} W_{41} x_1, \tag{3.11}$$

or

$$\begin{aligned} W_{71} = W_{76} W_{65} W_{54}(I - W_{46} W_{65} W_{54})^{-1} \\ \cdot W_{43} W_{32}(I - W_{23} W_{32})^{-1} W_{21}. \end{aligned} \tag{3.12}$$

If the stability of this system were to be analyzed, it would be unnecessary to proceed beyond figure 3.1, *c*, in the reduction. If all of the individual transmittances W_{ij} are stable, the stability of the system is then determined by the stability of the two self-loops of the essential diagram; that is, if the differential equations defined by

$$(I - W_{46}W_{64})^{-1} \tag{3.13}$$

and

$$(I - W_{23}W_{32})^{-1} \tag{3.14}$$

are stable, then the overall system is stable.

Since differential equations of self-loops are very important in feedback systems, a comment about their form is perhaps appropriate at this time. The differential equations of self-loops have the form

$$[I - W]^{-1}, \tag{3.15}$$

where W has the form of equation (3.2). Applying the method of addition of differential equations developed in chapter 2, the differential equation corresponding to equation (3.15) has the form

$$\sum_{i=0}^{n} [a_i(t) - b_i(t)] \frac{d^i y}{dt^i} = \sum_{i=0}^{n} a_i(t) \frac{d^i x}{dt^i}, \tag{3.16}$$

where y is the output and x is the input. The stability of the self-loop then depends on the stability of the homogeneous equation

$$\sum_{i=0}^{n} [a_i(t) - b_i(t)] \frac{d^i u}{dt^i} = 0. \tag{3.17}$$

In the next three sections the concepts of stability and sensitivity are examined, and an example is worked to show how they may be investigated by means of signal-flow graph concepts.

Stability

DEFINITION [ref. 12]. *A system is said to be stable if and only if every bounded input gives rise to a bounded output.*

The concept of the boundedness of the output of a system described by a differential equation can be explained as follows:

DEFINITION OF BOUNDEDNESS [ref. 4]. *Given a differential equation,*

$$y^{(n)} = f[t, y^{(1)}, \cdots, y^{(n-1)}], \tag{3.18}$$

a solution $y(t) = y(t; t_0, \eta_0, \cdots, \eta_{n-1})$ *is called "bounded at the right"*
if $\left| y^{(h)} \right| \leq M$, M *finite, for all* $t \geq t_0$, *and* $h = 0, 1, \cdots, n - 1$.

In the definition of boundedness, the η's represent the values of the initial conditions at time t_0. A definition analogous to this definition holds for "bounded at the left."

Two stability theorems that are useful in linear systems analysis are here stated. Theorem 3.1 can be used to determine the stability of a system described by a weighting function, and theorem 3.2 can be used to examine the stability of systems described by differential equations of the form in equation (3.1).

THEOREM 3.1. *A necessary and sufficient condition for a linear system described by a weighting function* $W(t, \tau)$ *to be stable is that*

$$\int_{-\infty}^{\infty} \left| W(t, \tau) \right| \, d\tau < constant < +\infty \text{ for all } t. \tag{3.19}$$

THEOREM 3.2 [ref. 4]. *Given the nth degree algebraic equation*

$$\lambda^n + \sum_{i=0}^{n-1} c_i \lambda^i = 0 \tag{3.20}$$

in which the c_i *are real constants, and* λ_i *for* $i = 1, \cdots, n$ *are solutions of the equation; and given the nth-order linear differential equation*

$$y^{(n)} + \sum_{i=0}^{n-1} a_i(t) y^{(i)} = F(t); \tag{3.21}$$

if $a_i(t) \to c_i$ *for* $i = 0, 1, \cdots, n - 1$, *if* $F(t) \to K$ *(a finite constant) as* $t \to +\infty$, *and if* $Re(\lambda_i) < 0$ *for* $i = 1, \cdots, n$, *then all solutions of equation* (3.21) *verify the relations* $y(t) \to K/c_0$, *and* $y^{(r)}(t) \to 0$ *for* $r = 1, \cdots, n$ *as* $t \to +\infty$. *If* $c_0 \neq 0$, $Re(\lambda_i) \leq 0$ *for* $i = 1, \cdots, n$ *and the roots with* $Re(\lambda_i) = 0$ *are simple, and if*

$$\int^{+\infty} \left| c_i - a_i(t) \right| \, dt < +\infty \quad \text{for} \quad i = 0, 1, \cdots, n - 1,$$

and

$$\int^{+\infty} \left| K - F(t) \right| \, dt < +\infty,$$

then all solutions of equation (3.21) *are bounded as* $t \to +\infty$. *The same holds if* $c_0 = 0$, *provided* $K = 0$.

Equation (3.1) can be written in the form of equation (3.21) if the definition

$$F(t) = \sum_{j=0}^{n} b_j(t) \frac{d^j x}{dt^j} \tag{3.22}$$

is used. It should be noted that the condition $F(t) \to K$ requires that $b_0(t) \to K_1$, $x(t) \to K_2$, and

$$\frac{d^j x}{dt^j} \to 0, \qquad j = 1, \cdots, n \quad \text{as} \quad t \to +\infty,$$

where K_1 and K_2 are finite constants and also that the $b_j(t)$ for $j = 1, \cdots, n$ be bounded as $t \to +\infty$.

SENSITIVITY

One measure of the quality of a feedback system is the sensitivity of the system to the variations of the system parameters. The sensitivity of an overall gain T with respect to a given parameter K can be defined by the equation

$$E_K^T = \frac{dT/T}{dK/K}. \tag{3.23}$$

In other words, the sensitivity of T with respect to K is the percentage change in T divided by the percentage change in K that causes the change in T, with all changes considered differentially small.

One factor which complicates the application of equation (3.23) to determine the sensitivity of a linear time-invariant system has been pointed out by Truxal [26]. In a general time-invariant system, the system transmittance T is a function of the complex frequency s (assuming the transmittance has been Laplace transformed). The sensitivity E_K^T will, therefore, also be a function of s. This means that the variation in the sensitivity results in a variation in the nature of the transient response. The significance of the dependence of the sensitivity of a time-invariant system upon the complex frequency s is relatively unknown. One result of this is that equation (3.23) is generally applied only to frequency independent gains T.

Suppose, however, a frequency dependent gain has been obtained for a linear time-invariant system. What can be done with it? First, an inverse transform can be applied and the equivalent time-varying sensitivity obtained that describes the system sensitivity for all time. In many cases, however, the only information that is desired is the "steady-state sensitivity" of the gain function.

The concept of a time-varying sensitivity can be extended directly to time-variable systems. It is obvious that even if a system has no dynamics, its sensitivity will be a function of time in the time-variable case. If the system has dynamics, then it is necessary to solve a linear time-variable differential equation to determine the sensitivity for all time. The steady-state sensitivity can be determined, however, by applying theorem 3.2 to the differential equation describing the sensitivity if the equation satisfies the theorem.

EXAMPLE

Consider a feedback system represented by the signal flow graph in

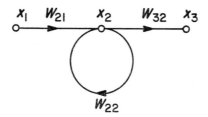

Figure 3.2. Example of technique.

figure 3.2. The various transmittances in figure 3.2 are given as follows: W_{21} represents the equation

$$x_2 = x_1; \tag{3.24}$$

W_{32} represents the equation

$$x_3 = x_2; \tag{3.25}$$

W_{22} represents the equation

$$\frac{d^2y}{dt^2} + a_1(t)\frac{dy}{dt} + a_0(t)y = b_1(t)\frac{dx_2}{dt} + b_0(t)x_2, \tag{3.26}$$

where

$$\begin{aligned}
a_1(t) &= 2 + e^{-t}, \\
a_0(t) &= 2 + e^{-2t}, \\
b_1(t) &= e^{-t} \\
b_0(t) &= 1.
\end{aligned} \tag{3.27}$$

Using the concepts developed in this chapter, the stability of the system and the steady-state sensitivity of the system to perturbations in $a_0(t)$ will be examined.

Applying the reduction techniques for self-loops, the differential equation relating x_1 and x_3 is found to be

$$\frac{d^2x_3}{dt^2} + [a_1(t) - b_1(t)]\frac{dx_3}{dt} + [a_0(t) - b_0(t)]x_3$$

$$= \frac{d^2x_1}{dt^2} + a_1(t)\frac{dx_1}{dt} + a_0(t)x_1. \quad (3.28)$$

Assuming that

$$\frac{d^2x_1}{dt^2} \; ; \qquad \frac{dx_1}{dt} \rightarrow 0$$

and $x_1 \rightarrow \bar{x}_1$ (a constant) as $t \rightarrow +\infty$, theorem 3.2 is applicable. It is seen that as $t \rightarrow +\infty$,

$$\begin{aligned}
[a_1(t) - b_1(t)] &= 2, \\
[a_0(t) - b_0(t)] &= 1 + e^{-2t} \rightarrow 1, \\
a_1(t) &= 2 + e^{-t} \rightarrow \bar{a}_1 = 2, \\
a_0(t) &= 2 + e^{-2t} \rightarrow \bar{a}_0 = 2.
\end{aligned} \qquad (3.29)$$

Therefore since the roots of

$$\lambda^2 + 2\lambda + 1 \qquad (3.30)$$

have negative real parts,

$$x_3(t) \rightarrow \bar{x}_3 = 2\bar{x}_1 \quad \text{as} \quad t \rightarrow +\infty, \qquad (3.31)$$

and the system is stable.

To determine the sensitivity of the output x_3 to a small change in a_0, assume that a_0 is perturbed to $a_0 + \delta a_0$ and that the output is perturbed to $x_3 + \delta x_3$. Substituting these values into equation (3.28), the following equation, in which second-order terms are neglected, is obtained:

$$\frac{d^2\delta x_3}{dt^2} + [a_1(t) - b_1(t)]\frac{d\delta x_3}{dt} + [a_0(t) - b_0(t)]\delta x_3$$

$$= \delta a_0[x_1 - x_3]. \quad (3.32)$$

Applying the conditions of equations (3.29) and theorem 3.2, the steady-state sensitivity of the system to a differentially small change in a_0 is

$$E_{a_0}^T = \frac{\overline{\delta x_3/x_3}}{\overline{\delta a_0/a_0}} = -\frac{\overline{a_0 x_1}}{x_3} = -1, \qquad (3.33)$$

where barred quantities are values approached as $t \rightarrow +\infty$.

SUMMARY

The purpose of this chapter was to show how the differential-equation algebra developed in chapter 2 can be applied as an aid in reducing and manipulating signal-flow graphs with transmittances that can be represented by ordinary linear time-variable differential equations. The concepts are useful because the ideas that have been developed for linear time-invariant flow graphs are readily extendable to linear time-variable flow graphs. Thus the analyst may use his knowledge of time-invariant systems in the analysis of time-variable systems through this parallel development.

Chapter 4

SYNTHESIS TECHNIQUES FOR LINEAR
TIME-VARIABLE FEEDBACK SYSTEMS

The phrase "synthesis of a system" implies literally that a designer proceeds logically in a step-by-step manner from a set of system specifications to a system that will meet these specifications. In this sense many of the design techniques for control systems are not true synthesis techniques. As examples, in the field of linear time-invariant control systems, the root-locus and frequency-domain methods are not true synthesis techniques. On the other hand, the design method proposed by Guillemin [26:279] in which the closed-loop transfer function is first determined from the specifications, and the compensation is determined subsequently, is a synthesis technique.

Synthesis techniques in the areas of nonlinear control and linear time-variable control are few and, generally, quite specialized. General synthesis techniques for feedback systems in either of these areas have not been developed. The reason for this is quite simple. General analytical techniques comparable to those available for time-invariant systems are not available for nonlinear systems and linear time-variable systems. The analytical techniques that are available are usually quite difficult, quite specialized, or both, and are not readily applicable to the synthesis problem.

Synthesis techniques for time-variable systems have tended to be less general than have the analytical techniques. One proposed approach synthesizes a given time-variable transfer function, or a given weighting function, as an open-loop system consisting of parallel elements of lower order [7], [8]. Another synthesis scheme allows a given time-variable weighting function to be synthesized as an open-loop system composed of analog computer elements [19]. Procedures that allow a time-variable system to be synthesized in the form of a feedback system are rare. Mal'chikov [18] proposed one procedure by means of which a given weighting function can be synthesized as a feedback system. The pro-

30

cedure is also applicable to the case where the system must contain a "fixed" plant. This method, however, has the disadvantage that certain integral equations must be solved in order to complete the synthesis.

In this chapter, two synthesis techniques will be developed using the differential-equation algebra developed in chapter 2. The first is a "plant cancellation" technique similar to the one for time-invariant systems discussed by Truxal [26:255]. The second method is an algebraic technique that gives an approximate solution. This technique is similar to that discussed in [17:238].

Synthesis by Plant Cancellation

Guillemin [26:279] in 1947 proposed that the synthesis of linear time-invariant feedback systems be accomplished in three steps as follows:

a. Determine the closed-loop transfer function from the specifications.
b. Find the corresponding open-loop transfer function.
c. Synthesize the appropriate compensation networks.

This synthesis technique is here generalized to include linear time-variable systems that may or may not be required to contain a fixed plant. The steps to follow for the time-variable case are these:

a. Determine the closed-loop weighting function, or closed-loop differential equation, from the specifications. (It is desirable to specify the system by its weighting function, since the system output for any input can then be determined by convolution.)
b. If the closed-loop weighting function has been specified, determine the corresponding closed-loop differential equation from the weighting function.
c. Determine the open-loop differential equation from the closed-loop differential equation.
d. Determine the differential equations for the appropriate compensation networks, and synthesize these networks by appropriate analog computer systems.

Implementation of this procedure requires techniques for (1) determining a weighting function, or differential equation, that meets the given specifications, and (2) manipulating this weighting function in such a way that the appropriate compensation networks can be developed. In chapter 5, (1) is considered in detail. In this chapter the application to (2) of the differential-equation algebra developed in chapter 2 is considered.

The application of the differential-equation algebra of chapter 2 to the synthesis problem is as straightforward conceptually as is the application of Laplace-transform algebra in the synthesis of linear time-invariant systems. The advantage of such an algebra is that all the manipula-

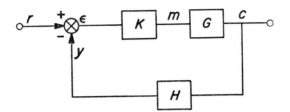

Figure 4.1. General feedback configuration.

tive operations can be performed symbolically and the numerical details carried out only at the end of the process.

To describe the technique of synthesis, the feedback configuration in figure 4.1 will be examined. In this figure r is the input, c is the output, and K, G, and H are differential equations. m and ϵ are intermediate variables in the system. In the following, the operation ($\cdot$) represents the operation which a differential equation performs on a variable to produce a new variable. Let the relationship between the output $r(t)$ and the input $c(t)$ be

$$c = W \cdot r, \tag{4.1}$$

where W is the desired overall differential equation. From figure 4.1 it is seen that

$$y = H \cdot c, \tag{4.2}$$

and

$$\epsilon = r - y = r - H \cdot c. \tag{4.3}$$

Since

$$m = K \cdot \epsilon, \quad \text{and} \quad c = G \cdot m, \tag{4.4}$$

it follows that

$$r = I \cdot \epsilon + HGK \cdot \epsilon = (I + HGK) \cdot \epsilon \tag{4.5}$$

by virtue of the fact that

$$I \cdot \epsilon = \epsilon. \tag{4.6}$$

Applying the multiplicative inverse of $(I + HGK)$ to both sides of (4.5) produces the equation

$$\epsilon = (I + HGK)^{-1} \cdot r. \tag{4.7}$$

Then, since

$$c = GK \cdot \epsilon, \tag{4.8}$$

substitution of (4.7) into (4.8) produces the equation

$$c = GK(I + HGK)^{-1} \cdot r. \tag{4.9}$$

Comparison of equations (4.1) and (4.9) reveals that

$$W = GK(I + HGK)^{-1}. \tag{4.10a}$$

Equation (4.10a) may be considered a fundamental relationship for figure 4.1.

From the identity (IV.1) in Appendix IV, W can also be represented in the form

$$W = (I + GKH)^{-1}GK. \tag{4.10b}$$

Thus a dual method for representing the results in the next two sections is possible. All fundamental relationships developed in those sections will be developed from both equations (4.10a) and (4.10b). Those developed from (4.10a) will be the (a) result and those developed from (4.10b) will be the (b) result. Two special cases of the configuration in figure 4.1 will now be considered.

SYNTHESIS OF A FEEDBACK SYSTEM
UNCONSTRAINED BY A FIXED PLANT

Suppose that a given overall differential equation W is to be realized as a feedback system with unity feedback; that is, it is to have the con-

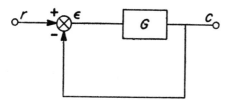

Figure 4.2. Unity feedback system.

figuration in figure 4.2. The synthesis problem is to determine G in terms of W. Since in this case

$$K = H = I, \tag{4.11}$$

equation (4.10) reduces to

$$W = G(I + G)^{-1}, \tag{4.12a}$$
$$W = (I + G)^{-1}G. \tag{4.12b}$$

Solving equations (4.12) for G, the relationships

$$G = (I - W)^{-1}W, \tag{4.13a}$$

$$G = W(I - W)^{-1} \tag{4.13b}$$

are obtained. Therefore a given differential equation W can be synthesized as a unity feedback system with G as the feedforward element through equations (4.13). The actual differential equation of G is obtained by performing the operations indicated in equations (4.13).

SYNTHESIS OF A SYSTEM CONSTRAINED BY A FIXED PLANT

In this case let W be the differential equation of the overall system of the configuration in figure 4.3. G is the differential equation of the known

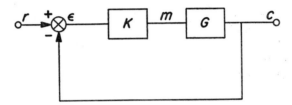

Figure 4.3. Feedback system with fixed plant.

fixed plant. The problem is to find the differential equation of a suitable compensation network K such that this system has the desired overall response indicated by W. Setting $H = I$ in equations (4.10) and solving for K, the relationships

$$K = G^{-1}(I - W)^{-1}W, \tag{4.14a}$$

$$K = G^{-1}W(I - W)^{-1} \tag{4.14b}$$

are formed. Performing the operations indicated symbolically in equations (4.14), the differential equation for K is obtained.

EXAMPLE

As an example of the process described above, consider the following problem. Suppose that G in figure 4.3 is a fixed plant described by the differential equation

$$\frac{d^2c}{dt^2} + \frac{dc}{dt} + e^{-t}c = m(t). \tag{4.15}$$

Let the desired overall differential equation W be

$$\frac{d^2c}{dt^2} + 2\frac{dc}{dt} + c = r. \tag{4.16}$$

$I - W$ is then formed by addition and is given by

$$\frac{d^2z}{dt^2} + 2\frac{dz}{dt} = \frac{d^2c}{dt^2} + 2\frac{dc}{dt} + c, \tag{4.17}$$

where z is the input and c is the output. The differential equation $(I - W)^{-1}W$ is then formed as

$$\frac{d^2c}{dt^2} + 2\frac{dc}{dt} = \epsilon(t). \tag{4.18}$$

The differential equation K is then produced from

$$K = G^{-1}(I - W)^{-1}W, \tag{4.19}$$

and the equation for this compensation network is found to be

$$\frac{d^2\epsilon}{dt^2} + \frac{2 + 3e^{-t}}{1 + e^{-t}}\frac{d\epsilon}{dt} + (1 + e^{-t})\epsilon$$

$$= \frac{d^2m}{dt^2} + \frac{3 + 4e^{-t}}{1 + e^{-t}}\frac{dm}{dt} + \frac{2 + 3e^{-t}}{1 + e^{-t}}m. \tag{4.20}$$

Thus the compensating network is completely specified by equation (4.20). This network can be synthesized by analog computer elements by the technique in Appendix III.

COMMENT

The disadvantages of this method of synthesis are the following:
1. Cancellation compensation ordinarily results in quite complex compensation networks.
2. Perfect cancellation is not possible because of practical considerations. (In the case of an unstable plant, this is a serious problem.)
3. By merely canceling the plant and putting in the desired open-loop transfer function, it is not possible to radically change the transfer characteristics of a system. Physical considerations will dictate the amount of change which is possible.

Even with these disadvantages the method is both straightforward and feasible from a practical viewpoint, and is therefore a valuable synthesis tool.

CONSTRAINTS ON THE CHOICE OF AN OVERALL DIFFERENTIAL EQUATION

In the choosing of an overall differential equation W, certain practical constraints on the form of the plant, the compensation network, and the overall system will restrict the relationship which may exist between the orders of the differential and integral operators of the compensation and the overall system. In general, it can be said that physical systems will have a smoothing effect on an input signal; that is, the system will usually contain at least one overall integration (the order of the integral operator is one greater than that of the differential operator). At the very least the orders of the integral and differential operators will be the same, and never will the order of the differential operator be greater than the order of the integral operator.

Examine equation (4.10) with $H = I$, that is, the equation

$$W = GK(I + GK)^{-1}. \tag{4.21}$$

By virtue of the previous discussion, the following restrictions will be placed on G and K. If G has the form

$$\sum_{i=0}^{N} a_i(t) \frac{d^i c}{dt^i} = \sum_{i=0}^{M} b_i(t) \frac{d^i m}{dt^i}, \tag{4.22}$$

where c is the output and m is the input, then $N > M$. If K has the form

$$\sum_{i=0}^{R} f_i(t) \frac{d^i m}{dt^i} = \sum_{i=0}^{P} d_i(t) \frac{d^i \epsilon}{dt^i}, \tag{4.23}$$

where m is the output and ϵ is the input, then $R \geq P$. The product GK then has the form

$$\sum_{i=0}^{N+R} g_i(t) \frac{d^i c}{dt^i} = \sum_{i=0}^{M+P} h_i(t) \frac{d^i \epsilon}{dt^i}, \tag{4.24}$$

where c is the output and ϵ is the input, and apparently $N + R > M + P$. Actually the orders of the operators in equation (4.24) will be given by $N + R - n$ and $M + P - n$, where n is the order of any terms common to both operators (see chap. 6). However, since the difference in these orders is unchanged by this reduction, it can be ignored in what follows. From equation (4.24) the equation $(I + GK)^{-1}$ can be written

$$\sum_{i=0}^{N+R} [g_i(t) + h_i(t)] \frac{d^i y}{dt^i} = \sum_{i=0}^{N+R} g_i(t) \frac{d^i x}{dt^i}, \tag{4.25}$$

where y is the output and x is the input. Finally, W can be formed by substituting equations (4.24) and (4.25) into (4.21), and W will have the form

$$\sum_{i=0}^{2(N+R)} p_i(t) \frac{d^i c}{dt^i} = \sum_{i=0}^{N+R+M+P} k_i(t) \frac{d^i r}{dt^i}. \tag{4.26}$$

From the constraints on N, M, R, and P,

$$2(N + R) - (N + R) - (M + P) \geqq N - M. \tag{4.27}$$

The relationship (4.27) then indicates that in choosing an overall differential equation W, it is necessary that the difference in orders of the integral and differential operators be equal to or greater than the difference in orders of the integral and differential operators of the fixed plant.

An Algebraic Synthesis Technique

The technique developed in this section closely resembles that developed in [17:238], which allows an overall system of the type in figure 4.3 to be synthesized approximately. The advantage of this technique is that the compensation network does not cancel the fixed plant. The basic equation for the technique is equation (4.14a), repeated here for convenience:

$$K = G^{-1}(I - W)^{-1}W. \tag{4.14a}$$

To aid in the development of this technique, each differential equation is factored into a differential operator premultiplied by an integral operator; that is,

$$K = I_k D_k,$$
$$G = I_g D_g, \tag{4.28}$$
$$W = I_w D_w.$$

Now if I (the unity element) is given the form

$$I = I_w I_w^{-1}, \tag{4.29}$$

then $(I - W)$ is given by

$$(I - W) = I_w(I_w^{-1} - D_w), \tag{4.30}$$

and

$$(I - W)^{-1} = (I_w^{-1} - D_w)^{-1} I_w^{-1}. \tag{4.31}$$

Substituting equations (4.28) and (4.31) into (4.14a), K is given by

$$K = I_k D_k = D_g^{-1} I_g^{-1}(I_w^{-1} - D_w)^{-1} I_w^{-1} I_w D_w \tag{4.32}$$

or

$$I_k D_k = D_g^{-1} I_g^{-1}(I_w^{-1} - D_w)^{-1} D_w. \tag{4.33}$$

At this point in the development a restriction is placed on K. It shall be required that K must not cancel the integral operator I_g of the plant.

This requirement prevents "cancellation" of the linearly independent solutions (of the differential equation) of the plant and substitution of a new set of dynamics. The restriction then requires that $(I_w^{-1} - D_w)^{-1}$ must satisfy the relationship

$$(I_w^{-1} - D_w)^{-1} = I_g I_c, \qquad (4.34)$$

where I_c is an as yet unknown integral operator. On substituting equation (4.34) into equation (4.33), we obtain

$$I_k D_k = D_g^{-1} I_c D_w. \qquad (4.35)$$

On equating integral and differential operators, we obtain

$$I_k = D_g^{-1} I_c, \qquad (4.36)$$

$$D_k = D_w. \qquad (4.37)$$

The equations that are used to determine the compensation are (4.34), rewritten in the form

$$I_w^{-1} = D_w + I_c^{-1} I_g^{-1}, \qquad (4.38)$$

and (4.36) and (4.37). In examining these equations, it must be remembered that I_g and D_g are known and fixed. Moreover, in determining an acceptable overall differential equation to meet the system specifications, it would be desirable if both I_w and D_w could be fixed, but this is not possible using this technique. Only I_w can be fixed from the specifications. This is equivalent to being able to fix the linearly independent solutions of the overall system weighting function but not being able to fix their multiplying constants; that is, D_w cannot be fixed. Thus in equation (4.38), I_w^{-1} and I_g^{-1} are known and D_w and I_c^{-1} are unknown differential operators that are to be determined by equating the coefficients of like derivatives on both sides of equation (4.38). Before this is done, however, certain constraints must be placed on the orders of the various differential and integral operators. To aid in the determination of these constraints, the following representations of various transmittances will be defined: Let W be the differential equation

$$\sum_{i=0}^{P_w} b_i(t) \frac{d^i c}{dt^i} = \sum_{i=0}^{Z_w} a_i(t) \frac{d^i r}{dt^i}, \qquad b_{P_w}(t) = 1. \qquad (4.39)$$

Let K be the differential equation

$$\sum_{i=0}^{P_k} h_i(t) \frac{d^i m}{dt^i} = \sum_{i=0}^{Z_k} g_i(t) \frac{d^i \epsilon}{dt^i}. \qquad (4.40)$$

Let G be the differential equation

$$\sum_{i=0}^{P_g} \beta_i(t) \frac{d^i c}{dt^i} = \sum_{i=0}^{Z_g} \alpha_i(t) \frac{d^i m}{dt^i}, \qquad \beta_{P_g}(t) = 1. \qquad (4.41)$$

Finally, let I_c be the differential equation

$$\sum_{i=0}^{P_c} f_i(t) \frac{d^i y}{dt^i} = x. \qquad (4.42)$$

As indicated previously, at this point the known I_w^{-1} is substituted into (4.38) from equation (4.39), the known I_g^{-1} is substituted into (4.38) from equation (4.41), and the representations of the unknown D_w and I_c are substituted into (4.38) from equations (4.39) and (4.42). The coefficients of like orders of derivatives are equated, and a set of simultaneous linear algebraic equations in the unknown $a_i(t)$ and $f_i(t)$ results. The solution of this set then produces the D_w and the I_c. In order for a solution to this equation to exist, the orders of the various operators are constrained as follows: On the basis of physical reasoning it is required that

$$P_w \geqq Z_w, \qquad P_g \geqq Z_g, \qquad P_k \geqq Z_k. \qquad (4.43)$$

From equation (4.38) it is seen that

$$P_c + P_g = P_w, \quad \text{or} \quad P_c = P_w - P_g. \qquad (4.44)$$

Upon equating like orders of derivatives in equation (4.38), a total of $P_w + 1$ equations in $Z_w + P_c + 2$ unknowns is obtained. For a solution to exist it is necessary that

$$P_w + 1 \leqq Z_w + P_c + 2,$$

or

$$P_w \leqq Z_w + P_c + 1. \qquad (4.45)$$

Substituting (4.44) into (4.45) it is seen that

$$Z_w \geqq P_g - 1. \qquad (4.46)$$

From condition (4.43) and equation (4.35),

$$Z_g + P_c = P_k \geqq Z_k = Z_w,$$

or

$$P_c \geqq Z_w - Z_g. \qquad (4.47)$$

Comparing equations (4.44) and (4.47),

$$P_w - P_g \geqq Z_w - Z_g,$$

or

$$P_w \geqq P_g + Z_w - Z_g. \tag{4.48}$$

Combining (4.46) and (4.48),

$$P_w \geqq 2P_g - Z_g - 1. \tag{4.49}$$

Conditions (4.44), (4.46), and (4.49) then restrict the orders of the operators P_w, Z_w, and P_c. The restriction on P_w must be taken into account when P_w is chosen to satisfy the system specifications. The conditions on Z_w and P_c are used to determine suitable forms for D_w and I_c in equation (4.38).

If in equations (4.46) and (4.49) the inequality is chosen, more unknowns than equations will be obtained. In this case it is possible to choose some of the unknowns in an arbitrary manner; for example, in a manner that allows optimization of some criterion function.

EXAMPLE

Suppose that a fixed plant is given by

$$\frac{d^2c}{dt^2} + \frac{dc}{dt} = m. \tag{4.50}$$

Thus

$$I_g \cdot c = \frac{d^2c}{dt^2} + \frac{dc}{dt} \quad \text{and} \quad D_g = 1. \tag{4.51}$$

Let the desired overall integral operator have the form

$$I_w \cdot c = \frac{d^3c}{dt^3} + e^{-t}\frac{d^2c}{dt^2} + \frac{dc}{dt} + e^{-2t}c, \tag{4.52}$$

which satisfies condition (4.49). Choosing

$$D_w = a_1(t)\frac{d}{dt} + a_0(t), \tag{4.53}$$

which satisfies condition (4.46), then I_c must have the form

$$I_c = b_1(t)\frac{d}{dt} + b_0(t). \tag{4.54}$$

Substituting (4.51), (4.52), (4.53), and (4.54) into (4.38), the relationship

$$\frac{d^3c}{dt^3} + e^{-t}\frac{d^2c}{dt^2} + \frac{dc}{dt} + e^{-2t}c$$

$$= b_1(t)\frac{d^3c}{dt^3} + [b_1(t) + b_0(t)]\frac{d^2c}{dt^3} \qquad (4.55)$$

$$+ [a_1(t) + b_0(t)]\frac{dc}{dt} + a_0(t)c$$

is formed.

Equating coefficients forms the simultaneous equations

$$\begin{aligned}
b_1(t) &= 1, \\
b_1(t) + b_0(t) &= e^{-t}, \\
a_1(t) + b_0(t) &= 1, \\
a_0(t) &= e^{-2t}.
\end{aligned} \qquad (4.56)$$

The solutions of equations (4.56) are

$$\begin{aligned}
b_1(t) &= 1, \\
b_0(t) &= e^{-t} - 1, \\
a_1(t) &= 2 - e^{-t}, \\
a_0(t) &= e^{-2t}.
\end{aligned}$$

The compensation network K is then given by

$$\frac{dm}{dt} + (e^{-t} - 1)m = (2 - e^{-t})\frac{d\epsilon}{dt} + (e^{-2t})\epsilon. \qquad (4.57)$$

COMMENT

The foregoing synthesis technique has two advantages:
1. The solution is simple.
2. A noncancellation compensation network is formed.
The disadvantages of this technique are the following:
1. The overall system response cannot be specified completely.
2. The form and the stability of the compensation network are not under the designer's control.

Chapter 5

THE APPROXIMATION PROBLEM

Before the synthesis techniques of chapter 4 can be used, an overall system weighting function which satisfies the system specifications must be determined. The problem of determining such a weighting function is called the approximation problem. For the synthesis techniques developed in chapter 4, it would be adequate to determine a system differential equation; it is, however, more desirable to know the system weighting function since the system output can then be determined for any input by application of the convolution integral.

There are many methods by which a system weighting function or a system differential equation might be obtained; for instance, the representation of the system might be given directly in the system specifications. In any event, once the form has been established, the procedures presented in the preceding chapter can be followed.

THE APPROXIMATION METHOD FOR POLYNOMIAL INPUTS

In this section, a method for determining weighting functions for a particular class of synthesis problems is presented. The method is restricted to systems which receive inputs that are expressed as polynomials in time and whose outputs can be approximated as a separable function [see equation (5.5)].

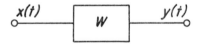

Figure 5.1. Linear system.

This approximation method can be formulated as follows: In figure 5.1 let $x(t)$ be a polynomial in time given by

$$x(t) = x(t - \tau) = \sum_{n=0}^{N} a_n(t - \tau)^n, \qquad t \geq \tau,$$

$$= 0, \qquad t < \tau.$$

$$(5.1)$$

where the a_n are constants, t is time, and τ is the time of application of $x(t)$ to the linear system W. $y(t)$ is the output of the linear system W that is produced as a result of the application of $x(t)$. It is assumed that an analytic expression for $y(t)$ can be determined from the specifications. W is the unknown linear system whose weighting function $W(t, \tau)$ it is desired to specify in a form that can be synthesized as a feedback system. From the convolution integral, $y(t)$ can be expressed as

$$y(t) = \int_{-\infty}^{t} W(t, \theta)x(\theta)\, d\theta. \tag{5.2}$$

Substituting equation (5.1) into equation (5.2), $y(t)$ becomes

$$y(t) = y_x(t, \tau) = \sum_{n=0}^{N} a_n \int_{\tau}^{t} W(t, \theta) \cdot (\theta - \tau)^n\, d\theta, \qquad t \geq \tau, \tag{5.3}$$

$$= 0, \qquad t < \tau.$$

The problem now reduces to that of solving the integral equation (5.3) for $W(t, \tau)$. Fortunately this equation reduces readily to an easily solved linear time-invariant differential equation. The class of $W(t, \tau)$ that is allowed is the class defined in chapter 1 by equations (1.1) and (1.2); that is, the class defined by weighting functions of the form

$$W(t, \tau) = W_1(t, \tau) + b_m(t)\delta(t - \tau), \qquad t \geq \tau,$$

$$= 0, \qquad t < \tau, \tag{5.4}$$

where

$$W_1(t, \tau) = \sum_{j=1}^{m} \beta_j(\tau)q_j(t), \qquad t \geq \tau,$$

$$= 0, \qquad t < \tau. \tag{5.5}$$

By requiring the q's to have $2m$ continuous derivatives and the β's to have m continuous derivatives, the technique of Appendix I can be applied to determine the differential equation that is equivalent to $W(t, \tau)$, which is

$$\sum_{i=0}^{m} c_i(t) \frac{\partial^i}{\partial t^i} [W(t, \tau)] = \sum_{j=0}^{m} b_j(t) \frac{\partial^j}{\partial t^j} [\delta(t - \tau)]. \tag{5.6}$$

Substituting equation (5.4) into equation (5.3), the relationship

$$y_x(t, \tau) = \sum_{n=0}^{N} a_n \int_{\tau}^{t} W_1(t, \tau)[\theta - \tau)^n\, d\theta$$

$$+ b_m(t) \sum_{n=0}^{N} a_n(t - \tau)^n \tag{5.7}$$

results. The solution of this equation will be broken into two parts: (1) determination of $b_m(t)$, and (2) determination of $W_1(t, \tau)$.

First, a technique for determining $b_m(t)$ will be presented. Assume that a_k $(0 \leq k \leq N)$ is that one of the nonzero a_n's with the lowest-valued subscript; that is,

$$y_x(t, \tau) = \sum_{n=k}^{N} a_n \int_{\tau}^{t} W_1(t, \theta)(\theta - \tau)^n \, d\theta$$

$$+ b_m(t) \sum_{n=k}^{N} a_n(t - \tau)^n. \qquad (5.8)$$

If now the kth partial derivative of $y_x(t, \tau)$ with respect to τ is formed, the relationship

$$\frac{\partial^k y_x(t, \tau)}{\partial \tau^k} = \sum_{n=k}^{N} a_n \int_{\tau}^{t} W_1(t, \theta)(-1)^k (n)(n-1) \cdots$$

$$\cdots (n - k + 1)(\theta - \tau)^{n-k} \, d\theta$$

$$+ b_m(t) \sum_{n=k}^{N} a_n(-1)^k (n)(n-1) \cdots$$

$$\cdots (n - k + 1)(t - \tau)^{n-k} \qquad (5.9)$$

results.

Now if the limit of

$$\frac{\partial^k y_x(t, \tau)}{\partial \tau^k}$$

as $\tau \to t$ is formed, the equation

$$\left. \frac{\partial^k y_x(t, \tau)}{\partial \tau^k} \right|_{\tau \to t} = b_m(t) a_k (-1)^k (k!) \qquad (5.10)$$

results. Solving equation (5.10) for $b_m(t)$, the desired relationship for $b_m(t)$ is obtained; that is,

$$b_m(t) = \frac{(-1)^k \left. \dfrac{\partial^k y_x(t, \tau)}{\partial \tau^k} \right|_{\tau \to t}}{(k!) a_k}. \qquad (5.11)$$

Once $b_m(t)$ is known, the expression

$$b_m(t) \sum_{n=0}^{N} a_n(t - \tau)^n \qquad (5.12)$$

can be formed, and a new function $y_x'(t, \tau)$ can be obtained from equation (5.8) as

$$y_x'(t, \tau) = y_x(t, \tau) - b_m(t) \sum_{n=0}^{N} a_n(t - \tau)^n$$

$$= \sum_{n=0}^{N} a_n \int_{\tau}^{t} W_1(t, \theta)(\theta - \tau)^n \, d\theta. \tag{5.13}$$

The second problem now is to determine $W_1(t, \tau)$ from equation (5.13). First, derivatives of $y_x'(t, \tau)$ with respect to τ are taken. The first derivative is

$$\frac{\partial y_x'(t, \tau)}{\partial \tau} = \sum_{n=0}^{N} a_n \int_{\tau}^{t} W_1(t, \theta)(-1)n(\theta - \tau)^{n-1} \, d\theta$$

$$- a_0 W_1(t, \tau). \tag{5.14}$$

The kth derivative $(k < N + 1)$ is

$$\frac{\partial^k y_x'(t, \tau)}{\partial \tau^k} = \sum_{n=0}^{N} a_n \int_{\tau}^{t} W_1(t, \theta)(-1)^k(n)(n - 1) \cdots$$

$$\cdots (n - k + 1)(\theta - \tau)^{n-k} \, d\theta$$

$$- \sum_{j=0}^{k-1} a_j \frac{\partial^{k-1-j} W_1(t, \tau)}{\partial \tau^{k-1-j}} (-1)^j(j!) \tag{5.15}$$

$$k = 1, 2, \cdots, N,$$

and the $(N + 1)$st is

$$\frac{\partial^{N+1} y_x'(t, \tau)}{\partial \tau^{N+1}} = \sum_{j=0}^{N} (-1)^{j+1}(j!)a_j \frac{\partial^{N-j} W_1(t, \tau)}{\partial \tau^{N-j}}. \tag{5.16}$$

Equation (5.16) is seen to be a linear time-invariant differential equation whose solution is $W_1(t, \tau)$. To solve this differential equation uniquely, N initial conditions must be obtained. Equations (5.15) produce these initial conditions if τ is made to approach t; that is,

$$\frac{\partial^k y_x'(t, \tau)}{\partial \tau^k}\bigg|_{\tau \to t} = \sum_{j=0}^{k-1} (-1)^{j+1}(j!)a_j \frac{\partial^{k-1-j} W_1(t, \tau)}{\partial \tau^{k-1-j}}\bigg|_{\tau \to t}, \tag{5.17}$$

or

$$\frac{\partial^{k-1} W_1(t, \tau)}{\partial \tau^{k-1}}\bigg|_{\tau \to t} = -\frac{1}{a_0}\left\{ \frac{\partial^k y_x'(t, \tau)}{\partial \tau^k}\bigg|_{\tau \to t} \right.$$

$$\left. - \sum_{j=1}^{k-1} (-1)^{j+1}(j!)a_j \frac{\partial^{k-1-j} W_1(t, \tau)}{\partial \tau^{k-1-j}}\bigg|_{\tau \to t} \right\}, \tag{5.18}$$

$$k = 1, 2, \cdots, N.$$

Equations (5.18) represent a set of recursive relationships that provide the N necessary "initial conditions." Actually since the derivatives of $W_1(t, \tau)$ are taken with respect to τ, equations (5.18) represent final conditions. This inconvenience is easily remedied by making the substitution

$$\tau = t - z \tag{5.19}$$

into equations (5.16) and (5.18). The resulting equations can then be easily solved, and by making the inverse substitution

$$z = t - \tau \tag{5.20}$$

into the solution obtained, $W_1(t, \tau)$ is recovered.

As a special case of this development, equations (5.11) and (5.16) are examined for the degenerate case of $x(t)$, namely,

$$x(t - \tau) = a_N(t - \tau)^N. \tag{5.21}$$

Equation (5.11) becomes

$$b_m(t) = \frac{(-1)^N \left. \dfrac{\partial^N y_z(t, \tau)}{\partial \tau^N} \right|_{\tau \to t}}{(N!)a_N}, \tag{5.22}$$

and equation (5.16) becomes

$$\frac{\partial^{N+1} y_z'(t, \tau)}{\partial \tau^{N+1}} = (-1)^{N+1}(N!)a_N W_1(t, \tau). \tag{5.23}$$

Equation (5.23) can be rewritten as

$$W_1(t, \tau) = \frac{(-1)^{N+1} \dfrac{\partial^{N+1} y_z'(t, \tau)}{\partial \tau^{N+1}}}{(N!)a_N}. \tag{5.24}$$

Equations (5.22) and (5.24) then should be used in the event that the input is a polynomial with but one nonzero coefficient. This case apparently includes step-function inputs.

It is obvious that in order for $W(t, \tau)$ to have the form indicated in equations (5.4) and (5.5), certain restrictions must be placed on the form of $y_z(t, \tau)$. Referring to equation (5.1), let $x_n(t - \tau) = a_n(t - \tau)^n$; then $x(t - \tau)$ can be rewritten

$$x(t - \tau) = \sum_{n=0}^{N} a_n(t - \tau)^n = \sum_{n=0}^{N} x_n(t - \tau). \tag{5.25}$$

Equation (5.3) then becomes

$$y_x(t, \tau) = \sum_{n=0}^{N} \int_{\tau}^{t} W(t, \theta) x_n(\theta - \tau) \, d\theta. \tag{5.26}$$

However, since $W(t, \tau)$ satisfies equation (5.6), $y_x(t, \tau)$ and $x(t - \tau)$ are related through the equation

$$
\begin{aligned}
\sum_{i=0}^{m} c_i(t) \frac{\partial^i y_x(t, \tau)}{\partial t^i} &= \sum_{j=0}^{m} b_j(t) \frac{\partial^j x(t - \tau)}{\partial t^j} \\
&= \sum_{j=0}^{m} \sum_{n=0}^{N} b_j(t) \frac{\partial^j x_n(t - \tau)}{\partial t^j} \\
&= \sum_{n=0}^{N} \sum_{j=0}^{m} b_j(t) \frac{\partial^j x_n(t - \tau)}{\partial t^j} .
\end{aligned}
\tag{5.27}
$$

Examination of the input $x(t - \tau)$, term by term, reveals that each $x_n(t - \tau) = a_n(t - \tau)^n$ can be formed by integrating the delta function $a_n(n!)\delta(t - \tau)$ a total of $n + 1$ times; that is,

$$x_n(t - \tau) = a_n(t - \tau)^n = \int \cdots \int a_n(n!)\delta(t - \tau)dt. \tag{5.28}$$

Using relationships (5.26), (5.27), and (5.28), a block diagram that corresponds to equation (5.27) can be drawn as shown in figure 5.2.

In figure 5.2, y_n is that part of the output $y(t)$ due to the $x_n(t - \tau)$

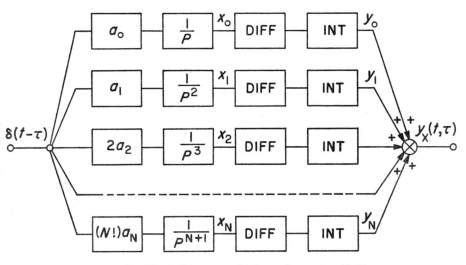

Figure 5.2. Block diagram equivalent of equation (5.27).

component of $x(t - \tau)$; that is,

$$y_x(t, \tau) = \sum_{n=0}^{N} y_n(t, \tau). \tag{5.29}$$

The notation $1/p^n$ within a box in figure 5.2 indicates that the input to the box is integrated n times. The system in figure 5.2 apparently represents a linear system with a delta function as an input and $y_x(t, \tau)$ as an output. Figure 5.3, a, represents the nth branch of the system in figure 5.2. Each branch then is seen to consist of a cascade combination of two linear differential equations. This combination can be replaced by a single differential equation (see chap. 2) as indicated in figure 5.3, b. Figure 5.2 is then equivalent to $N + 1$ parallel differential equations, and it can be replaced by a single equivalent linear differential equation (see

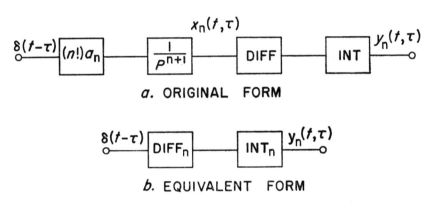

a. ORIGINAL FORM

b. EQUIVALENT FORM

Figure 5.3. The nth branch of figure 5.2.

chap. 2). Since the input to this system is a delta function and the output is $y_x(t, \tau)$, the latter is obviously the weighting function of the equivalent linear differential equation. The first requirement on $y_x(t, \tau)$, then, is that it must satisfy all the requirements of a weighting function; that is, it must be a separable function of t and τ with the form

$$y_x(t, \tau) = \sum_{j=1}^{M} \alpha_j'(\tau)u_j'(t), \qquad t \geq \tau,$$

$$= 0, \qquad t < \tau, \tag{5.30}$$

where the $\alpha_j'(\tau)$ are linearly independent, and the $u_j'(t)$ are linearly independent. Obviously $y_x'(t, \tau)$ [see equation (5.13)] will have the same form. The possibility of $y_x(t, \tau)$ containing singularity functions (i.e., delta functions or derivatives of delta functions) is dismissed since in practice outputs that are not continuous will not be encountered.

In addition to the requirement that $y_x(t, \tau)$ have the form indicated in equation (5.30), examination of equations (5.11), (5.16), and (5.18) reveals some additional requirements on $y_x(t, \tau)$. The solution for equation (5.16) has the form

$$W_1(t, \tau) = \sum_{i=1}^{N} c_i e^{-\gamma_i(t-\tau)}$$
$$+ \int_{t}^{\tau} G(\sigma - \tau)(-1)^N \frac{\partial^{N+1} y_x'(t, \sigma)}{\partial \sigma^{N+1}} \, d\sigma, \qquad (5.31)$$

where the c_i are functions of the initial conditions in equation (5.18); the $-\gamma$'s are roots of the polynomial

$$\sum_{j=0}^{N} (j!) a_j \gamma^{N-j} = 0, \qquad (5.32)$$

and $G(x - \theta)$ is the solution of the differential equation

$$\sum_{j=0}^{N} (j!) a_j \frac{\partial^{N-j} G(x - \theta)}{\partial x^{N-j}} = \delta(x - \theta). \qquad (5.33)$$

From equation (5.30), $y_x'(t, \sigma)$ will have the form

$$y_x'(t, \sigma) = \sum_{i=1}^{M} \alpha_j(\sigma) u_j(t), \qquad (5.34)$$

and

$$\frac{\partial^{N+1} y_x'(t, \sigma)}{\partial \sigma^{N+1}} = \sum_{i=1}^{M} \alpha_i^{(N+1)}(\sigma) u_i(t), \qquad (5.35)$$

where

$$\alpha_i^{(n)}(\sigma) = \frac{d^n \alpha_i(\sigma)}{d\sigma^n}.$$

If $G(\sigma - \tau)$ is written in its general exponential form as

$$G(\sigma - \tau) = \sum_{r=1}^{N} T_r e^{-\gamma_r(\sigma - \tau)}, \qquad (5.36)$$

then $W_1(t, \tau)$ can be written in the form

$$W_1(t, \tau) = \sum_{i=1}^{N} c_i(t) e^{-\gamma_i(t-\tau)}$$

$$+ \sum_{i=1}^{N} T_i e^{\gamma_i \tau} \int_t^{\tau} e^{-\gamma_i \sigma} (-1)^N$$

$$\cdot \sum_{j=1}^{M} \alpha_j{}^{(N+1)}(\sigma) u_j(t) \, d\sigma. \tag{5.37}$$

Rearranging equation (5.37),

$$W_1(t, \tau) = \sum_{i=1}^{N} e^{\gamma_i \tau} \left[c_i(t) e^{-\gamma_i t} + (-1)^{N+1} T_i \sum_{j=1}^{M} u_j(t) F_{ij}(t) \right]$$

$$+ \sum_{j=1}^{M} u_j(t) \left[(-1)^N \sum_{i=1}^{N} T_i e^{\gamma_i \tau} F_{ij}(\tau) \right], \tag{5.38}$$

where

$$F_{ij}(t) = \int^t e^{-\gamma_i \sigma} \alpha_j{}^{(N+1)}(\sigma) \, d\sigma. \tag{5.39}$$

Equation (5.38) indicates that $W_1(t, \tau)$ is a separable function of t and τ, with a maximum of $M + N$ terms; therefore it can be written

$$W_1(t, \tau) = \sum_{j=1}^{M+N} g_j(\tau) u_j(t), \tag{5.40}$$

where the g's and u's are defined according to equation (5.38). In order for $W_1(t, \tau)$ to be a weighting function of the type considered in equation (5.5), it is sufficient that the g's have $M + N$ continuous derivatives and the u's have $2(M + N)$ continuous derivatives. Applying these differentiability requirements to equation (5.38), it can be seen that the α's should have $2M + 3N$ continuous derivatives.

EXAMPLE

As an example of the technique just developed, consider the following problem: The input to a linear system has the form

$$x(t - \tau) = 2u(t - \tau) + (t - \tau) - 2(t - \tau)^2. \tag{5.41}$$

From the system specifications, the output of the system is required to have the form

$$y_x(t, \tau) = -\tfrac{7}{6}t^5 + t^4[\tfrac{5}{6} + \tfrac{10}{3}\tau] + t^3[1 - \tfrac{3}{2}\tau - 3\tau^2]$$
$$+ t^2[2\tau + \tfrac{1}{2}\tau^2 + \tfrac{2}{3}\tau^3 + 1]$$
$$+ t[-3\tau^2 + \tfrac{1}{6}\tau^3 + \tfrac{1}{6}\tau^4 - \tau + 2]. \tag{5.42}$$

Determine the weighting function $W(t, \tau)$, which represents the desired linear system, from the given input $x(t - \tau)$ and the desired output. It was shown that $W(t, \tau)$ can, in general, be divided into two parts; that is,

$$W(t, \tau) = W_1(t, \tau) + b_m(t)\delta(t - \tau). \tag{5.43}$$

The output $y_x(t, \tau)$ can then be represented by

$$y_x(t, \tau) = \sum_{n=0}^{N} a_n \int_{\tau}^{t} W_1(t, \theta)(\theta - \tau)^n \, d\theta$$
$$+ b_m(t) \sum_{n=0}^{N} a_n(t - \tau)^n, \tag{5.44}$$

where $N = 2$, $a_0 = 2$, $a_1 = 1$, and $a_2 = -2$.

The first step in determining $W(t, \tau)$ is to find $b_m(t)$. Taking the limit of $y_x(t, \tau)$ as $t \to \tau^+$, the relationship

$$\lim_{t \to \tau} y_x(t, \tau) = 2\tau = b_m(\tau)a_0 \tag{5.45}$$

is obtained. Therefore

$$b_m(t) = \frac{2t}{a_0} = t. \tag{5.46}$$

The second term of $y_x(t, \tau)$ in equation (5.44) is then

$$b_m(t) \sum_{n=0}^{N} a_n(t - \tau)^n = 2t + t^2 - t\tau - 2t^3 + 4t^2\tau - 2t\tau^2. \tag{5.47}$$

Inserting (5.47) into (5.44) and solving for $y_x'(t, \tau)$, which is given by

$$y_x'(t, \tau) = y_x(t, \tau) - b_m(t) \sum_{n=0}^{N} a_n(t - \tau)^n, \tag{5.48}$$

the equation

$$y_x'(t, \tau) = 3t^3 - \tfrac{3}{2}t^3\tau - 3t^3\tau^2 - 2t^2\tau + \tfrac{1}{2}t^2\tau^2 + \tfrac{2}{3}t^2\tau^3$$
$$+ \tfrac{5}{6}t^4 - \tfrac{10}{3}t^4\tau - t\tau^2 + \tfrac{1}{6}t\tau^3 + \tfrac{1}{6}t\tau^4 - \tfrac{7}{6}t^5 \tag{5.49}$$

is obtained. Next, the derivatives of $y_x'(t, \tau)$ with respect to τ are formed:

$$\frac{\partial y_x'}{\partial \tau} = -\tfrac{3}{2}t^3 - 6t^3\tau - 2t^2 + t^2\tau + 2t^2\tau^2 + \tfrac{10}{3}t^4 - 2t\tau$$

$$+ \tfrac{1}{2}t\tau^2 + \tfrac{2}{3}t\tau^3, \tag{5.50}$$

$$\frac{\partial^2 y_x'}{\partial \tau^2} = -6t^3 + t^2 + 4t^2\tau - 2t + t\tau + 2t\tau^2, \tag{5.51}$$

$$\frac{\partial^3 y_x'}{\partial \tau^3} = 4t^2 + t + 4t\tau. \tag{5.52}$$

Referring to equations (5.16) and (5.18), it can be seen that

$$\frac{\partial^3 y_x'(t, \tau)}{\partial \tau^3} = 4t^2 + t + 4t\tau = -2a_2 W_1(t, \tau)$$

$$+ a_1 \frac{\partial W_1(t, \tau)}{\partial \tau} - a_0 \frac{\partial^2 W_1(t, \tau)}{\partial \tau^2}, \tag{5.53}$$

$$W_1(t, t^-) = -\frac{1}{a_0}\left\{\frac{\partial y_x'(t, \tau)}{\partial \tau}\bigg|_{\tau \to t^-}\right\} = 2t^2, \tag{5.54}$$

$$\frac{\partial W_1(t, \tau)}{\partial \tau}\bigg|_{\tau \to t} = -\frac{1}{a_0}\left\{\frac{\partial^2 y_x'}{\partial \tau^2}\bigg|_{\tau \to t^-} - a_1 W_1(t, t^-)\right\} = t. \tag{5.55}$$

The solution of the set of equations (5.53), (5.54), and (5.55) then is the desired weighting function. To simplify the algebra involved and to make the solution of this set of equations easier, the following substitutions are made:

$$z = t - \tau,$$

$$k_2 = 2t,$$

$$k_1 = 4t^2 + \frac{t}{2}, \tag{5.56}$$

$$f(z) = W_1(t, t - z).$$

Then since $a_0 = 2$, $a_1 = 1$, and $a_2 = -2$, equations (5.53), (5.54), and (5.55) can be rewritten as

$$\frac{d^2 f}{dz^2} + \frac{1}{2}\frac{df}{dz} - 2f = k_2 z - k_1, \tag{5.53'}$$

$$f(0) = 2t^2, \tag{5.54'}$$

$$f'(0) = -t. \tag{5.55'}$$

The complementary solution of equation (5.53') has the form

$$f_c(z) = Ae^{-\gamma_1 z} + Be^{-\gamma_2 z}, \tag{5.57}$$

where A and B are functions of the initial conditions, and γ_1 and γ_2 are roots of the polynomial

$$\gamma^2 + \tfrac{1}{2}\gamma - 2 = 0. \tag{5.58}$$

The particular solution has the form

$$f_p = \frac{k_1}{2} - \frac{k_2}{8} - \frac{k_2}{2}z. \tag{5.59}$$

The entire solution then has the form

$$f(z) = Ae^{-\gamma_1 z} + Be^{-\gamma_2 z} + \frac{k_1}{2} - \frac{k_2}{8} - \frac{k_2}{2}z. \tag{5.60}$$

Applying the initial conditions of equations (5.54') and (5.55'), the constants A and B can be determined to be

$$A = \frac{\left[f(0) + \dfrac{k_2}{8} - \dfrac{k_1}{2}\right][-\gamma_2] - f'(0) - \dfrac{k_2}{2}}{\gamma_1 - \gamma_2}, \tag{5.61}$$

$$B = \frac{f'(0) + \dfrac{k_2}{2} + \gamma_1\left[f(0) + \dfrac{k_2}{8} - \dfrac{k_1}{2}\right]}{\gamma_1 - \gamma_2}. \tag{5.62}$$

Substituting the values from equations (5.54'), (5.55'), and (5.56) into (5.61) and (5.62), it can be shown that

$$A = 0 \quad \text{and} \quad B = 0; \tag{5.63}$$

$f(z)$ therefore equals the particular solution of the differential equation; that is,

$$f(z) = \frac{k_1}{2} - \frac{k_2}{8} - \frac{k_2}{2}z. \tag{5.64}$$

Substituting the values from equations (5.56) into (5.64), it can be shown that

$$W_1(t, \tau) = t^2 + t\tau. \tag{5.65}$$

The overall weighting function defined by equation (5.43) is then

$$W(t, \tau) = t^2 + t\tau + t\delta(t - \tau), \tag{5.66}$$

and the problem is solved. Convolution of (5.66) and (5.41) will indeed produce $y_x(t, \tau)$, as given in equation (5.42).

APPROXIMATION OF SEPARABLE FUNCTIONS

From the discussion in the previous section it is obvious that for a large class of synthesis problems the response function must have the form of a separable function that satisfies suitable differentiability conditions. In addition, the class of weighting functions considered in this monograph is a class of separable functions. It is necessary for the synthesis technique to include a method of approximating a function of two variables as a separable function of the two variables. Some work has been done on this problem; for instance, Cruz [6] proposed an impulse-train approximation of weighting functions; and Cruz and Van Valkenberg [8] proposed a method of approximating weighting functions as separable functions that approximate the weighting function (in some sense). The rest of this section describes a simple method of approximating a function of two variables as a separable function.

To help in explaining this approximation method, a final value controller will be considered. Suppose that a system is to be designed according to the following specifications: The system will receive a step input at an unknown time between $t = 0$ and $t = T$, and it is required that the system settle to within n percent of its final steady-state value (unity) by time T_s, where $T_s > T$. On the other hand, it is desirable to keep the system as sluggish as possible at all times. Thus if the system is designed as a linear time-variable system, the first step of the design is to determine a step response $y(t, \tau)$ that satisfies the specifications. The appropriate weighting function can be determined from this $y(t, \tau)$ and the design completed.

Figure 5.4 represents a two-dimensional view of $y(t, \tau)$ in which the τ-axis is perpendicular to the plane of the paper. The planes $y(t, 0)$ and $y(t, T)$ are the two planes which bound the region of interest of $y(t, \tau)$; that is, if the function $y(t, \tau)$ is suitable in this region the specifications can be met.

Suppose that $y(t, 0)$ and $y(t, T)$ are chosen with the form

$$y(t, 0) = 1 - e^{\alpha_1 t},$$
$$y(t, T) = 1 - e^{-\alpha_2 (t - T)},$$

(5.67)

where α_1 and α_2 are chosen so that

$$y(T_s, 0) = y(T_s, T) = 1 - \frac{n}{100}.$$

(5.68)

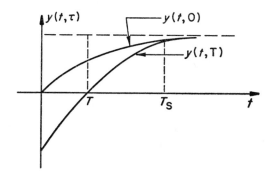

Figure 5.4. Two-dimensional view of $y(t, \tau)$.

It is seen then that $y(t, \tau)$ meets the specifications for two values of τ, namely, $\tau = 0$ and $\tau = T$. In addition $y(t, \tau)$ for $0 \leq \tau \leq T$ might be fixed for several additional values of τ; however, for the purpose of this exposition two will suffice. Obviously if $y(t, \tau)$ could be represented by relationships similar to equations (5.67) for all τ such that $0 \leq \tau \leq T$, the specifications could be met exactly. The number of values of τ for which $y(t, \tau)$ is fixed, for instance by equations (5.67), will also be the maximum number of terms in the final separable function; thus the better the desired approximation the higher the order of the resultant system.

Suppose figure 5.4 is redrawn as in figure 5.5, in which the t-axis is now normal to the plane of the paper. Outside the region where $0 \leq \tau \leq T$, $y(t, \tau)$ is arbitrary. At the boundaries of the region, $y(t, \tau)$ satisfies equations (5.67). If the only constraints on $y(t, \tau)$ are at $\tau = 0$ and $\tau = T$, $y(t, \tau)$ can be approximated in several ways. For instance, let

$$y(t, \tau) = y(t, 0) + [y(t, T) - y(t, 0)]u(\tau - T), \qquad (5.69)$$

where $u(\tau - T)$ is a step function occurring at $\tau = T$. Then $y(t, \tau)$ corresponds to the full line function in figure 5.5. If equation (5.69) is Laplace transformed with respect to τ, the resulting transform $Y(t, s)$ is

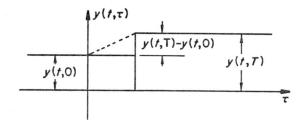

Figure 5.5. Approximation of $y(t, \tau)$.

given by

$$Y(t, s) = \frac{y(t, 0)}{s} + \frac{y(t, T) - y(t, 0)}{s} e^{-sT}. \tag{5.70}$$

Now if e^{-sT}/s is approximated by a Padé approximation [26:548], that is,

$$\frac{e^{-sT}}{s} \cong \frac{2(s - 3/T)}{Ts[s^2 + 4s/T + 6/T^2]}, \tag{5.71}$$

then

$$Y(t, s) \cong Y^*(t, s) = \frac{y(t, 0)}{s}$$
$$+ [y(t, T) - y(t, 0)]$$
$$\cdot \left\{ -\frac{2(s - 3/T)}{Ts[s^2 + 4s/T + 6/T^2]} \right\}. \tag{5.72}$$

The inverse transform of $Y^*(t, s)$ will be denoted $y^*(t, \tau)$. Other Padé approximations could be used in equation (5.70). Obviously a better approximation would be obtained if a higher-order polynomial were used. This approximation was chosen because it is relatively simple and because the numerator is of lesser degree than the denominator. The latter condition forces the second term of $y^*(t, \tau)$ to be zero at $\tau = 0$; hence, $y^*(t, 0) = y(t, 0)$. Taking the inverse transform of $Y^*(t, s)$, the approximation $y^*(t, \tau)$ is obtained as

$$y^*(t, \tau) = y(t, 0) \left[3e^{-2\tau/T} \sin\left(\frac{\sqrt{2}\tau}{T} + \psi\right) \right]$$
$$+ y(t, T) \left[1 - 3e^{-2\tau/T} \sin\left(\frac{\sqrt{2}\tau}{T} + \psi\right) \right]$$
$$t \geqq \tau, \tag{5.73}$$

where $\psi = \sin^{-1}(1/3)$, and $y(t, 0)$ and $y(t, T)$ are given in equation (5.67). This type of approximation plainly meets the differentiability requirements discussed in the previous section. As a very rough check on the accuracy of the approximation $y^*(t, \tau)$, it is seen that

$$y^*(t, 0) = y(t, 0),$$
$$y^*(t, T) = 0.398y(t, 0) + 0.602y(t, T), \tag{5.74}$$
$$y^*(t, \infty) = y(t, T).$$

The accuracy of this type of approximation can be improved by (1) approximating $y(t, \tau)$ by several steps in the τ direction (see fig. 5.5) [that is, let

$$y(t, \tau) = y(t, 0)$$

$$+ \sum_{n=1}^{N} \left\{ y\left(t, \frac{n}{N} T\right) - y\left[t, \left(\frac{n-1}{N}\right)T\right] \right\}$$

$$\cdot u\left(\tau - \frac{n}{N} T\right), \tag{5.75}$$

where N is an integer], and (2) using a higher order Padé approximation for $e^{-n/N(sT)}$.

Another possible method is to approximate a higher-order derivative of $y(t, \tau)$ as a series of step functions in the τ direction and then to integrate this function an appropriate number of times to regain $y(t, \tau)$. As an example, the derivative of the dotted-line representation of $y(t, \tau)$ in figure 5.5 is

$$y^{(0,1)}(t, \tau) = \frac{\partial}{\partial \tau} [y(t, \tau)]$$

$$= \frac{y(t, T) - y(t, 0)}{T} [u(\tau) - u(\tau - T)]. \tag{5.76}$$

If this equation is transformed, and if the Padé approximation in equation (5.71) is used, and then an inverse transform taken, the approximation of $y^{(0,1)}(t, \tau)$ that is denoted $y^{*(0,1)}(t, \tau)$ is given by

$$y^{*(0,1)}(t, \tau) = \frac{y(t, T) - y(t, 0)}{T}$$

$$\cdot 3e^{-2\tau/T} \sin\left[\frac{\sqrt{2}\tau}{T} + \psi\right], \tag{5.77}$$

where again $\psi = \sin^{-1}(1/3)$. Then, since

$$y^*(t, \tau) = y(t, 0) + \int_0^\tau y^{*(0,1)}(t, \theta) \, d\theta, \tag{5.78}$$

the final approximation is

$$y^*(t, \tau) = y(t, 0) e^{-2\tau/T} \left\{ \frac{1}{2} \sin \frac{\sqrt{2}\tau}{T} + \cos \frac{\sqrt{2}\tau}{T} \right\}$$

$$+ y(t, T) \left\{ 1 - e^{-2\tau/T} \left[\frac{1}{2} \sin \frac{\sqrt{2}\tau}{T} + \cos \frac{\sqrt{2}\tau}{T} \right] \right\},$$

$$t \geq \tau, \tag{5.79}$$

$$= 0, \quad t < \tau.$$

In comparison with the approximation of equation (5.73), it is seen that

$$y^*(t, 0) = y(t, 0),$$
$$y^*(t, T) = 0.116y(t, 0) + 0.884\ y(t, T), \qquad\qquad (5.80)$$
$$y^*(t, \infty) = y(t, T).$$

This procedure then produces a more accurate approximation to $y(t, \tau)$ than does the first procedure. An even more accurate one can be found if $\partial/\partial\tau[y(t, \tau)]$ is approximated by more terms, as is the case for $y(t, \tau)$ in the first procedure [see equation (5.75)].

While these approximating procedures leave something to be desired from the standpoint of mathematical sophistication, they are straight-forward and easily applied not only to weighting functions and step responses but also to polynomial responses that are also separable functions. The advantage of these methods is that the functions obtained always have enough differentiality to apply the methods developed in the preceding section.

AN APPROXIMATION METHOD FOR NONPOLYNOMIAL INPUTS

Again consider figure 5.1, which denotes a linear system with $y(t)$ as an output and $x(t)$ as an input. Suppose that $x(t)$ now is not a polynomial but a separable function of t and τ; that is, it can be represented by

$$x(t) = \sum_{n=0}^{N} a_n(\tau)x_n(t), \qquad t \geq \tau,$$
$$\qquad\qquad (5.81)$$
$$= 0, \qquad t < \tau.$$

Assume, also, that $y(t)$ can be expressed as a separable function of t and τ in accordance with the given system specifications; that is,

$$y(t) = \sum_{m=0}^{M} \alpha_m(\tau)y_m(t), \qquad t \geq \tau,$$
$$\qquad\qquad (5.82)$$
$$= 0, \qquad t < \tau.$$

Assuming there is enough differentiability of the $a_n(\tau)$, $x_n(t)$, $\alpha_m(\tau)$, and $y_m(t)$, equations (5.81) and (5.82) can both be assumed to be weighting functions of linear systems. Consequently, by the method of Appendix I, the differential equations that correspond to each can be determined. Figure 5.1 then could be redrawn as in figure 5.6. In figure 5.6, X repre-

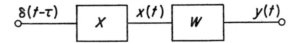

Figure 5.6. System equivalent to figure 5.1.

sents the differential equation corresponding to equation (5.81), and W represents the differential equation corresponding to the unknown system. If Y represents the differential equation corresponding to equation (5.82), then according to the notation of chapter 2,

$$Y = WX, \tag{5.83}$$

or

$$W = YX^{-1}. \tag{5.84}$$

Equation (5.84) indicates that if the input and output of an unknown linear system are known separable functions of t and τ, then the overall differential equation of the system can be determined by the product of Y and X^{-1}.

While this technique is more straightforward than that for polynomial inputs, the solution has less readily available information in it since it is in the form of a differential equation and not of a weighting function.

Chapter 6

REDUCIBILITY OF LINEAR SYSTEMS

Of major concern in the problem of synthesizing linear systems is whether or not the final form of the synthesized system is the simplest possible in terms of the number of elements required. In general, it is impossible to determine whether or not the simplest configuration has been found; any technique which may reduce the system complexity is therefore of value.

It is well known that the complexity of a linear system increases with the order of the differential equation which describes it; therefore one method of reducing the complexity of the system is to reduce the order of the differential equation which describes it prior to synthesis. The reduction must be done in such a way that the new lower-order differential equation is either

a. equivalent (definition to follow) to the original equation; or

b. an adequate approximation of the original equation.

This chapter is concerned with (a), that is, the problem of reducing, if possible, the original equation to an equivalent lower-order equation. A system for which this reduction is possible is called reducible, and the property of being reducible is called reducibility.

Equivalent Systems

The term equivalent in (a) is defined as follows:

DEFINITION. *Two linear systems are called equivalent if, whenever an input x is applied simultaneously to both systems, the outputs of the two systems are identical functions, say y(t).*

This definition assumes no initial conditions on the two systems.

Equivalent Differential Equations

A particular differential equation and several equations to which it is

60

equivalent are here examined.* The differential equation is

$$\sum_{i=0}^{n} a_i(t) \frac{d^i y}{dt^i} = \sum_{i=0}^{n} b_i(t) \frac{d^i x}{dt^i}, \qquad a_n(t) \equiv 1, \tag{6.1}$$

where x is the input and y is the output.

Any differential equation which is formed by operating on both sides of equation (6.1) with the same differential operator

$$\sum_{k=0}^{m} c_k(t) \frac{d^k}{dt^k}, \qquad c_m(t) \equiv 1, \tag{6.2}$$

is equivalent to equation (6.1), since y is still a solution of this equation if x is the input. Such an equation can be written

$$\sum_{k=0}^{m} c_k(t) \frac{d^k}{dt^k} \left[\sum_{i=0}^{n} a_i(t) \frac{d^i y}{dt^i} \right]$$

$$= \sum_{k=0}^{m} c_k(t) \frac{d^k}{dt^k} \left[\sum_{i=0}^{n} b_i(t) \frac{d^i x}{dt^i} \right], \tag{6.3}$$

and, if the indicated operations are carried out, equation (6.3) can be written

$$\sum_{i=0}^{m+n} g_i(t) \frac{d^i y}{dt^i} = \sum_{i=0}^{m+n} h_i(t) \frac{d^i x}{dt^i}, \tag{6.4}$$

where the $g_i(t)$ and $h_i(t)$ are defined appropriately. Equations (6.1), (6.3), and (6.4) are all equivalent.

Another equivalent form of equation (6.3), and hence of equations (6.1) and (6.4), is the pair of equations

$$\sum_{i=0}^{n} a_i(t) \frac{d^i y}{dt^i} = \sum_{i=0}^{n} b_i(t) \frac{d^i x}{dt^i} + z \tag{6.5}$$

and

$$\sum_{k=0}^{m} c_k(t) \frac{d^k z}{dt^k} = 0. \tag{6.6}$$

The equivalence of this pair of equations with equation (6.3) is shown by eliminating the variable z between the two equations, thus producing equation (6.3).

* In this chapter all coefficients are assumed analytic.

Equivalent Vector Forms

From the results of Appendix II, equation (6.1) can be written in the vector-matric form

$$y = (-1)^{n+1}[y_0 + \beta_n x],$$

$$
\begin{bmatrix} \dot{y}_0 \\ \dot{y}_1 \\ \cdot \\ \cdot \\ \dot{y}_{n-1} \end{bmatrix}
=
\begin{bmatrix}
\alpha_{n-1} & -1 & 0 & \cdots & 0 \\
\alpha_{n-2} & 0 & -1 & \cdots & 0 \\
\cdot & & & & \cdot \\
\cdot & & & & \cdot \\
\alpha_0 & 0 & 0 & \cdots & 0
\end{bmatrix}
\begin{bmatrix} y_0 \\ y_1 \\ \cdot \\ \cdot \\ y_{n-1} \end{bmatrix}
+
\begin{bmatrix} \beta_{n-1} \\ \beta_{n-2} \\ \cdot \\ \cdot \\ \beta_0 \end{bmatrix} x,
\qquad (6.7)
$$

or

$$\dot{\mathbf{y}} = \mathbf{A}\mathbf{y} + \boldsymbol{\beta} x, \qquad (6.8)$$

where a vector is in boldface lower case and a matrix in boldface capitals. Similarly, equation (6.3) [or equation (6.4)] can be written in the form

$$y = (-1)^{m+n+1}[u_0 + \delta_{m+n} x];$$

$$
\begin{bmatrix} \dot{u}_0 \\ \dot{u}_1 \\ \cdot \\ \cdot \\ \dot{u}_{m+n-1} \end{bmatrix}
=
\begin{bmatrix}
\gamma_{m+n-1} & -1 & 0 & \cdots & 0 \\
\gamma_{m+n-2} & 0 & -1 & \cdots & 0 \\
\cdot & & & & \cdot \\
\cdot & & & & \cdot \\
\gamma_0 & 0 & 0 & \cdots & 0
\end{bmatrix}
\cdot
\begin{bmatrix} u_0 \\ u_1 \\ \cdot \\ \cdot \\ u_{m+n-1} \end{bmatrix}
+
\begin{bmatrix} \delta_{m+n-1} \\ \delta_{m+n-2} \\ \cdot \\ \cdot \\ \delta_0 \end{bmatrix} x,
\qquad (6.9)
$$

or

$$\dot{\mathbf{u}} = \mathbf{G}\mathbf{u} + \boldsymbol{\delta} x. \qquad (6.10)$$

Similarly, the pair of equations (6.5) and (6.6) can be written as

$$y = (-1)^{n+1}[y_0 + \beta_n x],$$

$$
\begin{bmatrix} \dot{y}_0 \\ \dot{y}_1 \\ \cdot \\ \dot{y}_{n-1} \\ \dot{z}_0 \\ \dot{z}_1 \\ \cdot \\ \dot{z}_{m-1} \end{bmatrix}
=
\begin{bmatrix}
\alpha_{n-1} & -1 & 0 & \cdots & 0 & 0 & 0 & \cdots & 0 \\
\alpha_{n-2} & 0 & -1 & \cdots & 0 & 0 & 0 & \cdots & 0 \\
\cdot & & & & & & & & \cdot \\
\alpha_0 & 0 & 0 & \cdots & 0 & (-1)^{m+1} & 0 & & 0 \\
0 & 0 & 0 & \cdots & 0 & \eta_{m-1} & -1 & \cdots & 0 \\
0 & 0 & 0 & \cdots & 0 & \eta_{m-2} & 0 & \cdots & 0 \\
\cdot & & & & & \cdot & & & \cdot \\
0 & 0 & 0 & \cdots & 0 & \eta_0 & 0 & \cdots & 0
\end{bmatrix}
\begin{bmatrix} y_0 \\ y_1 \\ \cdot \\ y_{n-1} \\ z_0 \\ z_1 \\ \cdot \\ z_{m-1} \end{bmatrix}
+
\begin{bmatrix} \beta_{n-1} \\ \beta_{n-2} \\ \cdot \\ \beta_0 \\ 0 \\ 0 \\ \cdot \\ 0 \end{bmatrix} x.
\qquad (6.11)
$$

Equation (6.11) can further be written in the partitioned form

$$
\begin{bmatrix} \dot{\mathbf{y}} \\ \dot{\mathbf{z}} \end{bmatrix}
=
\begin{bmatrix} \mathbf{A} & \mathbf{M} \\ \mathbf{O} & \mathbf{H} \end{bmatrix}
\begin{bmatrix} \mathbf{y} \\ \mathbf{z} \end{bmatrix}
+
\begin{bmatrix} \boldsymbol{\beta} \\ \mathbf{0} \end{bmatrix} x.
\qquad (6.12)
$$

Since equations (6.1), (6.4), and the pair of equations (6.5) and (6.6) are equivalent, equations (6.7), (6.9), and (6.11) are equivalent [and (6.8), (6.10), and (6.12) are equivalent].

One more vector form equivalent to equations (6.8), (6.10), and (6.12) is necessary to the following development. It must be shown that a vector equation with the form of equation (6.12) can be changed by a linear transformation into an equation of the form

$$\dot{\omega} = \begin{bmatrix} \dot{\omega}_1 \\ \dot{\omega}_2 \end{bmatrix} = \begin{bmatrix} A' & M' \\ O & H' \end{bmatrix} \begin{bmatrix} \omega_1 \\ \omega_2 \end{bmatrix} + \begin{bmatrix} \beta' \\ 0 \end{bmatrix} x, \tag{6.13}$$

where

$$\beta' = \begin{bmatrix} 0 \\ 0 \\ \cdot \\ \cdot \\ \cdot \\ 1 \end{bmatrix} \qquad A' = \begin{bmatrix} \alpha'_{n-1} & -1 & 0 \cdots 0 \\ \alpha'_{n-2} & 0 & -1 \cdots 0 \\ \cdot & \cdot & \cdot & \cdot \\ \cdot & \cdot & \cdot & \cdot \\ \cdot & \cdot & \cdot & \cdot \\ \alpha'_0 & 0 & 0 \cdots 0 \end{bmatrix},$$

and M' and H' may have any form whatsoever so long as the equivalence of (6.12) and (6.13) is maintained. The transformation which transforms (6.12) into (6.13) has the form

$$\begin{bmatrix} y \\ z \end{bmatrix} = \begin{bmatrix} Q & O \\ O & P \end{bmatrix} \begin{bmatrix} \omega_1 \\ \omega_2 \end{bmatrix}, \tag{6.14}$$

where O represents an appropriately sized matrix of zeros. Substituting (6.14) into equation (6.12) produces the equation

$$\begin{bmatrix} \dot{\omega}_1 \\ \dot{\omega}_2 \end{bmatrix} = \left\{ \begin{bmatrix} Q^{-1} & O \\ O & P^{-1} \end{bmatrix} \begin{bmatrix} A & M \\ O & H \end{bmatrix} \begin{bmatrix} Q & O \\ O & P \end{bmatrix} \right.$$
$$- \begin{bmatrix} Q^{-1} & O \\ O & P^{-1} \end{bmatrix} \begin{bmatrix} \dot{Q} & O \\ O & \dot{P} \end{bmatrix} \right\} \begin{bmatrix} \omega_1 \\ \omega_2 \end{bmatrix}$$
$$+ \begin{bmatrix} Q^{-1} & O \\ O & P^{-1} \end{bmatrix} \begin{bmatrix} \beta \\ 0 \end{bmatrix} x. \tag{6.15}$$

Comparing equation (6.15) with (6.13), the following equations are obtained:

$$\begin{bmatrix} A & M \\ O & H \end{bmatrix} \begin{bmatrix} Q & O \\ O & P \end{bmatrix} - \begin{bmatrix} Q & O \\ O & \dot{P} \end{bmatrix} = \begin{bmatrix} Q & O \\ O & P \end{bmatrix} \begin{bmatrix} A' & M' \\ O & H' \end{bmatrix}, \tag{6.16}$$

and

$$\begin{bmatrix} \beta \\ 0 \end{bmatrix} = \begin{bmatrix} Q & O \\ O & P \end{bmatrix} \begin{bmatrix} \beta' \\ 0 \end{bmatrix}. \tag{6.17}$$

If the matrix $\mathbf{Q}$ is partitioned into its columns, that is,

$$\mathbf{Q} = [\mathbf{q}_1\ \mathbf{q}_2 \cdots \mathbf{q}_n], \qquad (6.18)$$

then, by the definition of β',

$$\mathbf{q}_n = \beta. \qquad (6.19)$$

Using the definitions of the matrices $\mathbf{Q}$ in (6.18) and $\mathbf{A}'$ in (6.13), the following equations in the unknown α_0', α_1', $\cdots$, α_{n-1}' of the matrix $\mathbf{A}'$ can be written

$$\mathbf{A}\mathbf{q}_1 - \dot{\mathbf{q}}_1 = \alpha_{n-1}'\mathbf{q}_1 + \alpha_{n-2}'\mathbf{q}_2 + \cdots + \alpha_0'\mathbf{q}_n, \qquad (6.20)$$

$$\mathbf{A}\mathbf{q}_2 - \dot{\mathbf{q}}_2 = -\mathbf{q}_1 \quad \text{or} \quad \mathbf{q}_1 = \dot{\mathbf{q}}_2 - \mathbf{A}\mathbf{q}_2,$$

$$\mathbf{A}\mathbf{q}_3 - \dot{\mathbf{q}}_3 = -\mathbf{q}_2 \quad \text{or} \quad \mathbf{q}_2 = \dot{\mathbf{q}}_3 - \mathbf{A}\mathbf{q}_3,$$

$$\cdots \cdots \cdots \cdots \cdots \cdots \qquad (6.21)$$

$$\mathbf{A}\mathbf{q}_n - \dot{\mathbf{q}}_n = -\mathbf{q}_{n-1} \quad \text{or} \quad \mathbf{q}_{n-1} = \dot{\mathbf{q}}_n - \mathbf{A}\mathbf{q}_n.$$

Thus from equations (6.19) and (6.21), the entire $\mathbf{Q}$ matrix can be determined, and equation (6.20) can be rewritten

$$\mathbf{Q}\begin{bmatrix} \alpha_{n-1}' \\ \vdots \\ \alpha_0' \end{bmatrix} = \mathbf{A}\mathbf{q}_1 - \dot{\mathbf{q}}_1. \qquad (6.22)$$

Then if the $\mathbf{Q}$ matrix is nonsingular, unknowns α_0', α_1', etc., can be calculated which satisfy equations (6.20) and (6.21), and the transformation indicated in equation (6.14) is possible. If the $\mathbf{Q}$ matrix is singular it will be shown subsequently that the system in (6.12) could have been changed to a form similar in structure to equation (6.12), in which the $\mathbf{A}$ matrix would have been of order less than $n \times n$.

REDUCIBILITY

A reducible equation can be defined as follows:

DEFINITION. *A reducible equation*

$$\dot{\mathbf{y}} = \mathbf{G}\mathbf{y} + \mathbf{f}x \qquad (6.23)$$

is an equation which can be transformed into the form

$$\dot{\mathbf{u}} = \begin{bmatrix} \dot{\mathbf{u}}_1 \\ \dot{\mathbf{u}}_2 \end{bmatrix} = \begin{bmatrix} \mathbf{X} & \mathbf{Y} \\ \mathbf{O} & \mathbf{Z} \end{bmatrix}\begin{bmatrix} \mathbf{u}_1 \\ \mathbf{u}_2 \end{bmatrix} + \begin{bmatrix} \mathbf{f}_1 \\ \mathbf{0} \end{bmatrix}x, \qquad (6.24)$$

where

$$\mathbf{y} = \mathbf{B}\mathbf{u}, \qquad (6.25)$$

and $\mathbf{B}$ is nonsingular.

In equation (6.24) only the $\mathbf{u}_1$ vector is dependent on x. Since the $\mathbf{u}_2$ vector is independent of x, it can be disregarded in examining the equivalence of equations (6.23) and (6.24), since the definition of equivalence is concerned only with the forced response of the two systems produced by x. Therefore the equation

$$\dot{\mathbf{u}}_1 = \mathbf{X}\mathbf{u}_1 + \mathbf{f}_1 x \tag{6.26}$$

is equivalent to equation (6.23) by virtue of the relationship (6.24), in which

$$\mathbf{u} = \begin{bmatrix} \mathbf{u}_1 \\ 0 \end{bmatrix}. \tag{6.27}$$

At this point it is necessary to develop the following:
a. Conditions on $\mathbf{G}$ and $\mathbf{f}$ in equation (6.23) that indicate whether or not such an equation is reducible.
b. A technique for producing the matrix $\mathbf{B}$ that will allow reduction of a reducible system in the form of (6.23) to an equivalent reduced system in the form of equation (6.26). In particular the reduced form of the equation will have the reduced form of equation (6.13),

$$\dot{\omega}_1 = \mathbf{A}'\omega_1 + \beta' x. \tag{6.28}$$

Since (a) and (b) are intermeshed, they will be accomplished simultaneously in what follows.

CONDITIONS AND TECHNIQUE FOR REDUCTION

In equation (6.13) let

$$\mathbf{A} = \begin{bmatrix} \mathbf{A}' & \mathbf{M}' \\ \mathbf{O} & \mathbf{H}' \end{bmatrix} \quad \text{and} \quad \mathbf{g} = \begin{bmatrix} \beta' \\ 0 \end{bmatrix}. \tag{6.29}$$

If equation (6.23) is reducible, then equations (6.23) and (6.13) must be equivalent through the relationship

$$\mathbf{y} = \mathbf{C}\omega, \tag{6.30}$$

where $\mathbf{C}$ is nonsingular. Substituting (6.30) into (6.23) and comparing the result with equation (6.13), the following equations are obtained:

$$\mathbf{A} = \mathbf{C}^{-1}\mathbf{G}\mathbf{C} - \mathbf{C}^{-1}\dot{\mathbf{C}}, \tag{6.31}$$

and

$$\mathbf{g} = \mathbf{C}^{-1}\mathbf{f}. \tag{6.32}$$

Now if the $(m + n) \times (m + n)$ matrix

$$\mathbf{P} = [\mathbf{g}, \mathbf{A}\mathbf{g}, \mathbf{A}^2\mathbf{g}, \cdots, \mathbf{A}^{m+n-1}\mathbf{g}] \tag{6.33}$$

is formed, it is seen, by virtue of the definitions for $\mathbf{A}$ and $\mathbf{g}$ in equation (6.13), to have the form

$$
\mathbf{P} = \left.\begin{bmatrix}
0 & 0 & 0 \cdots & 0 & (-1)^{n-1} & (-1)^{n-1}\alpha'_{n-1} \cdots \\
0 & 0 & 0 \cdots (-1)^{n-2} & 0 & (-1)^{n-1}\alpha'_{n-2} \cdots \\
\cdot & \cdot & \cdot & \cdot & \cdot & \cdot \\
0 & -1 & 0 & 0 & 0 & (-1)^{n-1}\alpha'_1 \cdots \\
1 & 0 & 0 \cdots & 0 & 0 & (-1)^{n-1}\alpha'_0 \cdots \\
0 & 0 & 0 \cdots & 0 & 0 & 0 \\
\cdot & \cdot & \cdot & \cdot & \cdot & \cdot \\
0 & 0 & 0 & 0 & 0 & 0 \cdots
\end{bmatrix}\right\} n \text{ rows}
\tag{6.34}
$$

$$
\underbrace{\qquad\qquad}_{n \text{ columns}} \quad \underbrace{\qquad\qquad}_{m \text{ columns}}
$$

The $\mathbf{P}$ matrix obviously has rank n, its first n columns are linearly independent, and its $(n+1)$st column is a linear combination of the first n.

In terms of the relationships (6.31) and (6.32), the $\mathbf{P}$ matrix can be written

$$
\mathbf{P} = \mathbf{C}^{-1}[\mathbf{f}, \, [\mathbf{G} - \dot{\mathbf{C}}\mathbf{C}^{-1}]\mathbf{f}, \, [\mathbf{G} - \dot{\mathbf{C}}\mathbf{C}^{-1}]^2\mathbf{f}, \, \cdots
$$
$$
\cdots, [\mathbf{G} - \dot{\mathbf{C}}\mathbf{C}^{-1}]^{m+n-1}\mathbf{f}] \tag{6.35}
$$

by virtue of the fact that

$$
\mathbf{A}^i\mathbf{g} = [\mathbf{C}^{-1}\mathbf{G}\mathbf{C} - \mathbf{C}^{-1}\dot{\mathbf{C}}]^i\mathbf{C}^{-1}\mathbf{f} = \mathbf{C}^{-1}[\mathbf{G} - \dot{\mathbf{C}}\mathbf{C}^{-1}]^i\mathbf{f}. \tag{6.36}
$$

Since $\mathbf{C}$ is nonsingular and is an $(n+m) \times (n+m)$ matrix, and since $\mathbf{P}$ has rank n and its first n columns are linearly independent, the matrix

$$
\mathbf{P}' = \mathbf{C}\mathbf{P} = [\mathbf{f}, \, [\mathbf{G} - \dot{\mathbf{C}}\mathbf{C}^{-1}]\mathbf{f}, \, \cdots, [\mathbf{G} - \dot{\mathbf{C}}\mathbf{C}^{-1}]^{m+n-1}\mathbf{f}] \tag{6.37}
$$

must have rank n, and its first n columns must be linearly independent.

At this point let the $\mathbf{C}$ matrix be partitioned into an $(m+n) \times n$ matrix $\boldsymbol{\Gamma}$ and an $(m+n) \times m$ matrix $\mathbf{B}$; that is,

$$
\mathbf{C} = [\boldsymbol{\Gamma} \; \mathbf{B}]. \tag{6.38}
$$

Using this representation, equations (6.31) and (6.32) can be rewritten as

$$
\mathbf{G}[\boldsymbol{\Gamma} \; \mathbf{B}] - [\dot{\boldsymbol{\Gamma}} \; \dot{\mathbf{B}}] = [\boldsymbol{\Gamma} \; \mathbf{B}]\begin{bmatrix} \mathbf{A}' & \mathbf{M}' \\ 0 & \mathbf{H}' \end{bmatrix}, \tag{6.39}
$$

and

$$
\mathbf{f} = [\boldsymbol{\Gamma} \; \mathbf{B}]\mathbf{g} = \boldsymbol{\Gamma}\boldsymbol{\beta}', \tag{6.40}
$$

by virtue of the definition of $\mathbf{g}$.

Equation (6.39) can be further rewritten as two equations:

$$
\mathbf{G}\boldsymbol{\Gamma} - \dot{\boldsymbol{\Gamma}} = \boldsymbol{\Gamma}\mathbf{A}', \tag{6.41a}
$$

$$
\mathbf{G}\mathbf{B} - \dot{\mathbf{B}} = \boldsymbol{\Gamma}\mathbf{M}' + \mathbf{B}\mathbf{H}'. \tag{6.41b}
$$

If $\boldsymbol{\Gamma}$ is now partitioned into its n columns; that is,

$$\boldsymbol{\Gamma} = [\boldsymbol{\gamma}_1, \boldsymbol{\gamma}_2, \cdots, \boldsymbol{\gamma}_n], \tag{6.42}$$

then equations (6.40) and (6.41a) can be written in expanded form as

$$\mathbf{f} = \boldsymbol{\gamma}_n, \tag{6.43}$$

$$\mathbf{G}\boldsymbol{\gamma}_1 - \dot{\boldsymbol{\gamma}}_1 = \alpha'_{n-1}\boldsymbol{\gamma}_1 + \alpha'_{n-2}\boldsymbol{\gamma}_2 + \cdots + \alpha'_0\boldsymbol{\gamma}_n, \tag{6.44}$$

$$\mathbf{G}\boldsymbol{\gamma}_2 - \dot{\boldsymbol{\gamma}}_2 = -\boldsymbol{\gamma}_1 \quad \text{or} \quad \boldsymbol{\gamma}_1 = \dot{\boldsymbol{\gamma}}_2 - \mathbf{G}\boldsymbol{\gamma}_2,$$

$$\mathbf{G}\boldsymbol{\gamma}_3 - \dot{\boldsymbol{\gamma}}_3 = -\boldsymbol{\gamma}_2 \quad \text{or} \quad \boldsymbol{\gamma}_2 = \dot{\boldsymbol{\gamma}}_3 - \mathbf{G}\boldsymbol{\gamma}_3,$$

$$\cdots \cdots \qquad \cdots \cdots \cdots \tag{6.45}$$

$$\mathbf{G}\boldsymbol{\gamma}_n - \dot{\boldsymbol{\gamma}}_n = -\boldsymbol{\gamma}_{n-1} \quad \text{or} \quad \boldsymbol{\gamma}_{n-1} = \dot{\boldsymbol{\gamma}}_n - \mathbf{G}\dot{\boldsymbol{\gamma}}_n,$$

by virtue of the definition of $\mathbf{A}'$ and $\boldsymbol{\beta}'$. Relationships (6.43) and (6.45) suffice to specify the $\boldsymbol{\Gamma}$ matrix.

Using relations (6.43) and (6.45), it is now possible to return to the $\mathbf{P}'$ matrix and deduce conditions on $\mathbf{G}$ and $\mathbf{f}$ that indicate the reducibility of a system. The first column of the $\mathbf{P}'$ matrix is $\mathbf{f}$ and is fixed. Now examine the second column,

$$[\mathbf{G} - \dot{\mathbf{C}}\mathbf{C}^{-1}]\mathbf{f} = \mathbf{G}\mathbf{f} - \dot{\mathbf{C}}\mathbf{C}^{-1}\mathbf{f}. \tag{6.46}$$

From the relationships (6.32) and (6.29) and the definition of $\boldsymbol{\beta}'$,

$$\mathbf{C}^{-1}\mathbf{f} = \begin{bmatrix} 0 \\ \vdots \\ 0 \\ 1 \\ 0 \\ \vdots \\ 0 \end{bmatrix} \left.\vphantom{\begin{bmatrix} 0 \\ \vdots \\ 0 \end{bmatrix}}\right\} n \text{ components} \tag{6.47}$$

and

$$\dot{\mathbf{C}}\mathbf{C}^{-1}\mathbf{f} = \dot{\boldsymbol{\gamma}}_n = \dot{\mathbf{f}}; \tag{6.48}$$

therefore

$$\mathbf{G}\mathbf{f} - \dot{\mathbf{C}}\mathbf{C}^{-1}\mathbf{f} = \mathbf{G}\mathbf{f} - \dot{\mathbf{f}} = \mathbf{G}\boldsymbol{\gamma}_n - \dot{\boldsymbol{\gamma}}_n = -\boldsymbol{\gamma}_{n-1}. \tag{6.49}$$

The third column is then given by

$$[\mathbf{G} - \dot{\mathbf{C}}\mathbf{C}^{-1}][-\boldsymbol{\gamma}_{n-1}] = -[\mathbf{G} - \dot{\mathbf{C}}\mathbf{C}^{-1}]\boldsymbol{\gamma}_{n-1}$$

$$= -[\mathbf{G}\boldsymbol{\gamma}_{n-1} - \dot{\mathbf{C}}\mathbf{C}^{-1}\boldsymbol{\gamma}_{n-1}]. \tag{6.50}$$

Now examine the term

$$\dot{C}C^{-1}\gamma_{n-1}. \tag{6.51}$$

By the definition of γ_{n-1}, it is apparent that

$$C^{-1}\gamma_{n-1} = \begin{bmatrix} 0 \\ \cdot \\ \cdot \\ \cdot \\ 1 \\ 0 \\ \cdot \\ \cdot \\ \cdot \\ 0 \end{bmatrix} \Big\} \ n-1 \text{ elements} \tag{6.52}$$

and consequently

$$\dot{C}C^{-1}\gamma_{n-1} = \dot{\gamma}_{n-1}. \tag{6.53}$$

The third column of the P' matrix can then be written

$$-[G\gamma_{n-1} - \dot{\gamma}_{n-1}] = \gamma_{n-2}. \tag{6.54}$$

In a similar manner it can be shown that the third column is $-\gamma_{n-3}$, the fourth is γ_{n-4}, and so forth; therefore the first n columns of the P' matrix are

$$\gamma_n, \ -\gamma_{n-1}, \ \gamma_{n-2}, \ \cdots, \ (-1)^{n-1}\gamma_1. \tag{6.55}$$

The $(n+1)$st column, which must be a linear combination of the first n columns, is given as

$$(-1)^n[G - \dot{C}C^{-1}]\gamma_1 = (-1)^n[G\gamma_1 - \dot{\gamma}_1]$$
$$= \alpha'_{n-1}\gamma_1 + \cdots + \alpha'_0\gamma_n. \tag{6.56}$$

Note that by use of equation (6.56) it is possible to solve for the α's.

It is apparent from equations (6.39) and (6.40) that the forms desired for the A matrix,

$$A = \begin{bmatrix} A' & M' \\ O & H' \end{bmatrix}, \tag{6.57}$$

and the g vector,

$$g = \begin{bmatrix} 0 \\ 0 \\ \cdot \\ \cdot \\ \cdot \\ 1 \\ 0 \\ \cdot \\ \cdot \\ \cdot \\ 0 \end{bmatrix}, \tag{6.58}$$

are independent of the **B** part of the **C** matrix. Thus the **B** matrix is chosen in such a way that the **C** matrix is nonsingular, but it may otherwise have any form at all.

The rules then for testing the reducibility and for reducing, if possible, the vector differential equation

$$\dot{\mathbf{y}} = \mathbf{G}\mathbf{y} + \mathbf{f}x, \quad \text{where} \quad \mathbf{y} \text{ is an } N \text{ vector}, \tag{6.59}$$

are as follows:

1. Form the $N \times N$ matrix

$$\mathbf{P}' = [\gamma_N, -\gamma_{N-1}, \gamma_{N-2}, \cdots, (-1)^{N-1}\gamma_1], \tag{6.60}$$

   where

   $\gamma_N = \mathbf{f}$ and

   $\gamma_i = \dot{\gamma}_{i+1} - \mathbf{G}\gamma_{i+1}.$

2. Test the rank of $\mathbf{P}'$; if it is equal to N, the system is not reducible.
3. If the rank of the $\mathbf{P}'$ matrix is $n < N$, then the system can be reduced to an equivalent system of order n,

$$\dot{\omega} = \mathbf{A}'\omega + \beta'x, \tag{6.61}$$

where
$$\mathbf{y} = \Gamma\omega, \tag{6.62}$$

$\mathbf{A}'$ is an $n \times n$ matrix defined by the partitioning

$$\begin{bmatrix} \mathbf{A}' & \mathbf{M}' \\ 0 & \mathbf{H}' \end{bmatrix} = [\mathbf{C}^{-1}\mathbf{G}\mathbf{C} - \mathbf{C}^{-1}\dot{\mathbf{C}}], \tag{6.63}$$

$$\beta' = \begin{bmatrix} 0 \\ 0 \\ 0 \\ 0 \\ \cdot \\ \cdot \\ 1 \end{bmatrix} \quad \text{is an } n\text{-vector},$$

and
$$\mathbf{C} = [\gamma_{N-m}, \gamma_{N-m+1}, \cdots, \gamma_N, \beta_{n+1}, \beta_{n+2}, \cdots, \beta_N], \tag{6.64}$$

where

$\gamma_N = \mathbf{f},$

$\gamma_{N-1} = \dot{\gamma}_N - \mathbf{G}\gamma_N,$

$\gamma_{N-2} = \dot{\gamma}_{N-1} - \mathbf{G}\gamma_{N-1},$

$\cdots \cdots \cdots \cdots$

$\gamma_{N-m} = \dot{\gamma}_{N-m+1} - \mathbf{G}\gamma_{N-m+1},$

and the β's are arbitrary vectors chosen so that **C** is nonsingular.

EXAMPLES

Example 1. Examine the reducibility of the linear constant coefficient differential equation

$$\ddot{y} + 3\dot{y} + 2y = \ddot{x} + 2\dot{x} + x, \tag{6.65}$$

and, if possible, find an equivalent reduced form. Using the technique developed in Appendix II, this equation can be written in the vector form

$$\begin{bmatrix} \dot{y}_0 \\ \dot{y}_1 \end{bmatrix} = \begin{bmatrix} -3 & -1 \\ 2 & 0 \end{bmatrix} \begin{bmatrix} y_0 \\ y_1 \end{bmatrix} + \begin{bmatrix} 1 \\ -1 \end{bmatrix} x, \tag{6.66}$$

where $y = -y_0 + x$.

Following the procedure outlined, the matrix

$$\mathbf{P}' = [\gamma_2 \ -\gamma_1] = \begin{bmatrix} 1 & +2 \\ -1 & -2 \end{bmatrix} \tag{6.67}$$

is formed. It is obvious that $\gamma_1 = -2\gamma_2$, and $\mathbf{P}'$ has rank 1; therefore equation (6.65) is reducible. To reduce it, the **C** matrix is formed using γ_2 for the first column and an arbitrary vector for the second (one which prevents **C** from being singular); that is,

$$\mathbf{C} = \begin{bmatrix} 1 & 1 \\ -1 & 0 \end{bmatrix}. \tag{6.68}$$

Then

$$\mathbf{C}^{-1} = \begin{bmatrix} 0 & -1 \\ 1 & 1 \end{bmatrix}. \tag{6.69}$$

The new equation equivalent to equation (6.66) is then

$$\begin{bmatrix} \dot{u}_0 \\ \dot{u}_1 \end{bmatrix} = \begin{bmatrix} 0 & -1 \\ 1 & 1 \end{bmatrix} \begin{bmatrix} -3 & -1 \\ 2 & 0 \end{bmatrix} \begin{bmatrix} 1 & 1 \\ -1 & 0 \end{bmatrix} \begin{bmatrix} u_0 \\ u_1 \end{bmatrix}$$
$$+ \begin{bmatrix} 0 & -1 \\ 1 & 1 \end{bmatrix} \begin{bmatrix} 1 \\ -1 \end{bmatrix} x, \tag{6.70}$$

or

$$\begin{bmatrix} \dot{u}_0 \\ \dot{u}_1 \end{bmatrix} = \begin{bmatrix} -2 & -2 \\ 0 & -1 \end{bmatrix} \begin{bmatrix} u_0 \\ u_1 \end{bmatrix} + \begin{bmatrix} 1 \\ 0 \end{bmatrix} x. \tag{6.71}$$

From equation (6.71) the lower-order equation equivalent to equation (6.66) is

$$\dot{u}_0 = -2u_0 + x, \tag{6.72}$$

where, assuming $u_1 \equiv 0$,

$$y_0 = u_0, \tag{6.73}$$

and

$$y = -u_0 + x \quad \text{or} \quad u_0 = -y + x. \tag{6.74}$$

Substituting equation (6.74) into (6.72), an equation in y is formed; that is,

$$\dot{y} + 2y = \dot{x} + x, \tag{6.75}$$

which is equivalent to equation (6.65). In this simple example the same result could have been obtained by examining the roots of the polynomial operators of equation (6.65), that is, the roots of

$$(P^2 + 3P + 2)y = (P^2 + 2P + 1)x, \tag{6.76}$$

or

$$(P + 2)(P + 1)y = (P + 1)(P + 1)x,$$

where $P = d/dt$.

Cancellation of the common $(P + 1)$ root would produce equation (6.75) directly. In higher-order equations, however, the latter procedure is not so readily apparent.

It should be noted before leaving this example that the equation for u_1 in (6.71) contains the common root $(P + 1)$ in equation (6.65); that is,

$$(P + 1)u_1 = 0, \tag{6.77}$$

where $P = d/dt$.

Example 2. Examine the reducibility, and reduce, if possible, the equation

$$\dddot{x} + (1 + e^{-t})\ddot{x} + (1 + e^{-t})\dot{x} + e^{-t}x = \dot{y} + e^{-t}y. \tag{6.78}$$

Using the technique of Appendix II, equation (6.78) can be written in vector form as

$$\dot{\mathbf{y}} = \begin{bmatrix} \dot{y} \\ \dot{y}_1 \\ \dot{y}_2 \end{bmatrix} = \begin{bmatrix} -(1 + e^{-t}) & -1 & 0 \\ (1 + 3e^{-t}) & 0 & -1 \\ -3e^{-t} & 0 & 0 \end{bmatrix} \begin{bmatrix} y \\ y_1 \\ y_2 \end{bmatrix} + \begin{bmatrix} 0 \\ -1 \\ e^{-t} \end{bmatrix} x. \tag{6.79}$$

To test the reducibility of (6.79), the $\mathbf{P}'$ matrix is formed from the γ vectors

$$\gamma_3 = \begin{bmatrix} 0 \\ -1 \\ e^{-t} \end{bmatrix},$$

$$\gamma_2 = \begin{bmatrix} -1 \\ e^{-t} \\ -e^{-t} \end{bmatrix}, \tag{6.80}$$

$$\gamma_1 = \begin{bmatrix} -1 \\ 1 + e^{-t} \\ -2e^{-t} \end{bmatrix},$$

and

$$\mathbf{P}' = [\gamma_3 \; -\gamma_2 \; \gamma_1]. \tag{6.81}$$

Obviously $\gamma_1 = \gamma_2 - \gamma_3$, the rank of $\mathbf{P}'$ is 2, and equation (6.79) is reducible. The $\mathbf{C}$ matrix can be formed as

$$\mathbf{C} = \begin{bmatrix} -1 & 0 & 0 \\ e^{-t} & -1 & 0 \\ -e^{-t} & e^{-t} & 1 \end{bmatrix}; \tag{6.82}$$

further,

$$\mathbf{C}^{-1} = \begin{bmatrix} -1 & 0 & 0 \\ -e^{-t} & -1 & 0 \\ (e^{-2t} - e^{-t}) & e^{-t} & 1 \end{bmatrix}, \tag{6.83}$$

and

$$\dot{\mathbf{C}} = \begin{bmatrix} 0 & 0 & 0 \\ -e^{-t} & 0 & 0 \\ e^{-t} & -e^{-t} & 0 \end{bmatrix}. \tag{6.84}$$

An equation equivalent to (6.79) can now be formed by the relations

$$\dot{u} = \mathbf{A}u + gx, \tag{6.85}$$

where

$$y = Cu,$$

$$A = C^{-1} \begin{bmatrix} -(1 + e^{-t}) & -1 & 0 \\ (1 + 3e^{-t}) & 0 & -1 \\ -3e^{-t} & 0 & 0 \end{bmatrix} C - C^{-1}\dot{C}, \qquad (6.86)$$

and

$$g = C^{-1} \begin{bmatrix} 0 \\ -1 \\ e^{-t} \end{bmatrix}. \qquad (6.87)$$

Substitution of relations (6.82), (6.83), and (6.84) into (6.86) and (6.87) gives

$$A = \begin{bmatrix} -1 & -1 & 0 \\ 1 & 0 & 1 \\ 0 & 0 & -e^{-t} \end{bmatrix}, \qquad (6.88)$$

and

$$g = \begin{bmatrix} 0 \\ 1 \\ 0 \end{bmatrix}. \qquad (6.89)$$

The reduced equation equivalent to (6.79) is then

$$\begin{bmatrix} \dot{u}_0 \\ \dot{u}_1 \end{bmatrix} = \begin{bmatrix} -1 & -1 \\ 1 & 0 \end{bmatrix} \begin{bmatrix} u_0 \\ u_1 \end{bmatrix} + \begin{bmatrix} 0 \\ 1 \end{bmatrix} x, \qquad (6.90)$$

where, from (6.82),

$$y = -u_0. \qquad (6.91)$$

Eliminating u_1 and u_0 between equations (6.90) and (6.91) produces the differential equation

$$\ddot{y} + \dot{y} + y = x, \qquad (6.92)$$

which is equivalent to equation (6.78). The equivalence is apparent if both sides of (6.92) are operated upon by the operator

$$\left(\frac{d}{dt} + e^{-t} \right). \qquad (6.93)$$

Summary

In this chapter a method of reducing the order of certain linear systems has been presented. The technique is useful because the lower-order system can be synthesized with fewer elements than the original system. In practice this could result in a great saving in the cost of a particular system.

Chapter 7

APPROXIMATIONS
OF DIFFERENTIAL EQUATIONS

In the last chapter, the concept of the equivalence of differential equations was discussed. It was shown that under certain conditions a differential equation might be replaced by a lower-order differential equation to which it is equivalent. While the concept of equivalence is valuable, its value is limited by the fact that a differential equation may not have a lower-order equivalent. This limitation notwithstanding, it may, at times, be necessary to replace a particular differential equation by a lower-order differential equation whether or not it has an equivalent. If it does not, then the lower-order differential equation is an approximation.

A second instance that necessitates an approximation of a differential equation occurs because of practical constraints on the difference in the orders of the integral and differential operators of physical systems. These constraints, which were discussed in chapter 4, require that (1) the order of the integral operator of a physical system be greater than, or equal to, the order of the differential operator of the system; and (2) the difference in the orders of the integral and differential operators of an overall feedback system must be greater than or equal to the difference in the orders of the integral and differential operators of the open-loop system. In the case in which a particular differential equation does not meet these requirements, it is necessary, in some manner, to increase the difference in the orders of the integral and differential operators without appreciably changing the response characteristics of the differential equation.

APPROXIMATION BY A LOWER-ORDER DIFFERENTIAL EQUATION

In chapter 6, the concept of reducibility was discussed. Conditions were developed that an $(m + n)$th-order vector equation of the form

$$\dot{\mathbf{y}} = \mathbf{G}\mathbf{y} + \mathbf{f}x \qquad (7.1)$$

must satisfy in order for it to be reduced to an equivalent lower-order (say nth-order) differential equation. These conditions might be stated as follows: If the equation

$$GC - \dot{C} = CA \tag{7.2}$$

has a solution C such that the following requirements are satisfied, then equation (7.1) is reducible to an nth-order vector equation. These requirements follow:

1. The matrix A, in partitioned form, can be written

$$A = \begin{bmatrix} Q & M \\ O & H \end{bmatrix}, \tag{7.3}$$

where Q is an $n \times n$ matrix, O an $m \times n$ zero matrix, and M and H are similarly defined.
2. The nth column of the matrix C is the vector f.
3. The matrix C is nonsingular.

The question that now arises is: If equation (7.1) is *not* reducible— that is, a C matrix cannot be found which satisfies these conditions—how can an approximate solution to equation (7.2) be obtained such that an nth-order vector equation is formed which approximates equation (7.1)? This question will occupy the rest of this section.

Let the C matrix be partitioned into two submatrices: Γ, an $(m + n) \times n$ matrix, and B, an $(m + n) \times m$ matrix; that is,

$$C = [\Gamma \ B]. \tag{7.4}$$

Then if equations (7.3) and (7.4) are substituted into equation (7.2), two equations are formed:

$$G\Gamma - \dot{\Gamma} = \Gamma Q, \tag{7.5}$$
$$GB - \dot{B} = \Gamma M + BH. \tag{7.6}$$

If a best (in some sense) approximate solution to equations (7.5) and (7.6), subject to the constraint that the nth column of the matrix Γ is f, is found, then the differential equation which results will be called an approximation of equation (7.1).

To obtain a best approximate solution of equations (7.5) and (7.6), let the matrices Q and Γ be defined as follows:

$$Q = \begin{bmatrix} \alpha_1 & -1 & 0 \cdots 0 \\ \alpha_2 & 0 & -1 \cdots 0 \\ \vdots & \vdots & \vdots \quad \vdots \\ \alpha_n & 0 & 0 \cdots 0 \end{bmatrix}, \tag{7.7}$$

$$\mathbf{\Gamma} = [\gamma_1, \gamma_2, \cdots, \gamma_n]. \tag{7.8}$$

Using these definitions plus the fact that $\gamma_n = \mathbf{f}$, equation (7.5) can be written as the set of equations

$$\mathbf{G}\gamma_1 - \dot{\gamma}_1 = \alpha_1\gamma_1 + \alpha_2\gamma_2 + \cdots + \alpha_n\gamma_n, \tag{7.9}$$

$$
\begin{aligned}
\gamma_1 &= \dot{\gamma}_2 - \mathbf{G}\gamma_2, \\
\gamma_2 &= \dot{\gamma}_3 - \mathbf{G}\dot{\gamma}_3, \\
&\vdots \\
\gamma_{n-1} &= \dot{\gamma}_n - \mathbf{G}\gamma_n, \\
\gamma_n &= \mathbf{f}.
\end{aligned}
\tag{7.10}
$$

Equation (7.9) can be rewritten

$$\mathbf{\Gamma}\boldsymbol{\alpha} = \mathbf{G}\gamma_1 - \dot{\gamma}_1, \tag{7.11}$$

where

$$\boldsymbol{\alpha} = \begin{bmatrix} \alpha_1 \\ \alpha_2 \\ \vdots \\ \alpha_n \end{bmatrix}.$$

In Appendix V it is shown that the best approximate solution, in the least-squares sense, of equation (7.11) is determined by solving the equation

$$\mathbf{\Gamma}^T \mathbf{\Gamma}\boldsymbol{\alpha} = \mathbf{\Gamma}^T\mathbf{G}\gamma_1 - \mathbf{\Gamma}^T\dot{\gamma}_1, \tag{7.12}$$

where $\mathbf{\Gamma}^T$ is the transpose matrix of $\mathbf{\Gamma}$. It should be noted that if the differential equation is reducible, then the $\boldsymbol{\alpha}$ vector is an exact solution of equation (7.11).

Having obtained the approximate solution for equation (7.5), the next step is to find a solution for equation (7.6). An exact (though not unique) solution for equation (7.6) can be found in the following manner: Let $\mathbf{M}$ and $\mathbf{H}$ have the forms

$$\mathbf{M} = \begin{bmatrix} \mu_1 & 0 & 0 & \cdots & 0 \\ \mu_2 & 0 & 0 & \cdots & 0 \\ \vdots & \vdots & \vdots & & \vdots \\ \mu_n & 0 & 0 & \cdots & 0 \end{bmatrix}, \tag{7.13}$$

and

$$H = \begin{bmatrix} \eta_1 & -1 & 0 \cdots 0 \\ \eta_2 & 0 & -1 \cdots 0 \\ \vdots & \vdots & \vdots \\ \eta_m & 0 & 0 \cdots 0 \end{bmatrix}.$$ (7.14)

B is then partitioned into columns as follows:

$$B = [\beta_1, \beta_2, \cdots, \beta_m].$$ (7.15)

Then, by virtue of equations (7.13), (7.14) and (7.15), equation (7.6) can be written as the set of equations

$$G\beta_1 - \dot{\beta}_1 = \mu_1\gamma_1 + \mu_2\gamma_2 + \cdots + \mu_n\gamma_n$$
$$+ \eta_1\beta_1 + \cdots + \eta_m\beta_m,$$ (7.16)

$$\beta_1 = \dot{\beta}_2 - G\beta_2,$$
$$\beta_2 = \dot{\beta}_3 - G\beta_3,$$ (7.17)
$$\vdots$$
$$\beta_{m-1} = \dot{\beta}_m - G\beta_m.$$

Now β_m can be chosen arbitrarily with the single constraint that the matrix

$$C = [\Gamma \; B]$$ (7.18)

is not singular. From β_m and G, the B matrix is completely specified through equations (7.17). Equation (7.16) can then be written

$$[\Gamma \; B] \begin{bmatrix} \mu \\ n \end{bmatrix} = G\beta_1 - \dot{\beta}_1,$$ (7.19)

where

$$\mu = \begin{bmatrix} \mu_1 \\ \mu_2 \\ \vdots \\ \mu_n \end{bmatrix}, \quad \text{and} \quad n = \begin{bmatrix} \eta_1 \\ \eta_2 \\ \vdots \\ \eta_m \end{bmatrix}.$$

Equation (7.19) then can be solved exactly for μ, and n, since the matrix $[\Gamma \; B]$ is nonsingular.

The *reduced form* of the approximation of equation (7.1) then has the form

$$\begin{bmatrix} \dot{u}_1' \\ \dot{u}_2' \end{bmatrix} = \begin{bmatrix} Q & M \\ O & H \end{bmatrix} \begin{bmatrix} u_1' \\ u_2' \end{bmatrix} + \begin{bmatrix} f_1 \\ 0 \end{bmatrix} x,$$ (7.20)

where

$$\mathbf{f}_1 = \begin{bmatrix} 0 \\ 0 \\ \cdot \\ \cdot \\ \cdot \\ 0 \\ 1 \end{bmatrix}.$$

Equation (7.20) can now be written as

$$\dot{\mathbf{u}}' = \mathbf{A}'\mathbf{u}' + \mathbf{f}'x. \tag{7.21}$$

The approximation of equation (7.1) is next represented by

$$\dot{\mathbf{y}}' = \mathbf{G}'\mathbf{y}' + \mathbf{f}x, \tag{7.22}$$

where, by virtue of relationship (7.2),

$$\mathbf{G}' = \mathbf{C}\mathbf{A}'\mathbf{C}^{-1} + \dot{\mathbf{C}}\mathbf{C}^{-1}. \tag{7.23}$$

Since

$$\mathbf{y}' = \mathbf{C}\mathbf{u}', \tag{7.24}$$

and

$$\mathbf{y}' = [\mathbf{\Gamma}\ \mathbf{B}]\begin{bmatrix} \mathbf{u}_1' \\ \mathbf{u}_2' \end{bmatrix}, \tag{7.25}$$

the approximate reduced form of equation (7.1) is given by the equations

$$\dot{\mathbf{u}}_1' = \mathbf{Q}\mathbf{u}_1' + \mathbf{f}_1 x \tag{7.26}$$

and

$$\mathbf{y}' = \mathbf{\Gamma}\mathbf{u}_1'. \tag{7.27}$$

In order to evaluate a particular approximation, some measure of the error vector $\boldsymbol{\varepsilon} = \mathbf{y} - \mathbf{y}'$ should be obtained. When an exact numerical solution can be calculated, there is no problem evaluating the error. For many cases obtaining a solution proves too burdensome; therefore an error bound has been developed to aid in evaluating the approximate equation (see Appendix VI).

Example

As an example of the approximation technique just described, a first-order approximation of the vector equation

$$\begin{bmatrix} \dot{y}_0 \\ \dot{y}_1 \end{bmatrix} = \begin{bmatrix} -3 & 1 \\ -(2 + e^{-t}) & 0 \end{bmatrix}\begin{bmatrix} y_0 \\ y_1 \end{bmatrix} + \begin{bmatrix} 1 \\ 2 \end{bmatrix}x, \tag{7.28}$$

or

$$\dot{\mathbf{y}} = \mathbf{G}\mathbf{y} + \mathbf{f}x, \tag{7.29}$$

will be found.

The first step of the procedure is to let

$$\gamma = \mathbf{f} = \begin{bmatrix} 1 \\ 2 \end{bmatrix}, \tag{7.30}$$

as indicated in equation (7.10). Next, the equation

$$\mathbf{G}\gamma - \dot{\gamma} = \alpha\gamma \tag{7.31}$$

is formed in accordance with equation (7.9). This equation is

$$\begin{bmatrix} -1 \\ -(2 + e^{-t}) \end{bmatrix} = \alpha \begin{bmatrix} 1 \\ 2 \end{bmatrix}, \tag{7.32}$$

and obviously has no solution. Using the technique in Appendix V, the best least-squares approximation for α is found by the equation

$$[1 \ 2] \begin{bmatrix} 1 \\ 2 \end{bmatrix} \alpha = [1 \ 2] \begin{bmatrix} -1 \\ -(2 + e^{-t}) \end{bmatrix}, \tag{7.33}$$

or

$$5\alpha = -5 - 2e^{-t}. \tag{7.34}$$

Then

$$\alpha = -1 - 2/5e^{-t}. \tag{7.35}$$

Next, according to equation (7.17) and the remark that follows it, β is chosen arbitrarily as

$$\beta = \begin{bmatrix} 0 \\ 1 \end{bmatrix}. \tag{7.36}$$

Then from equations (7.30) and (7.36), the matrix $\mathbf{C}$ is given by

$$\mathbf{C} = \begin{bmatrix} 1 & 0 \\ 2 & 1 \end{bmatrix}, \tag{7.37}$$

and

$$\mathbf{C}^{-1} = \begin{bmatrix} 1 & 0 \\ -2 & 1 \end{bmatrix}. \tag{7.38}$$

Now equation (7.19) is formed as

$$\begin{bmatrix} 1 & 0 \\ 2 & 1 \end{bmatrix}\begin{bmatrix} \mu \\ \eta \end{bmatrix} = \begin{bmatrix} 1 \\ 0 \end{bmatrix}. \tag{7.39}$$

From equation (7.39),

$$\mu = 1 \quad \text{and} \quad \eta = -2. \tag{7.40}$$

From equations (7.35) and (7.40), the approximate reducible equation has the form

$$\begin{bmatrix} \dot{u}_1' \\ \dot{u}_2' \end{bmatrix} = \begin{bmatrix} -(1 + 2/5e^{-t}) & 1 \\ 0 & -2 \end{bmatrix}\begin{bmatrix} u_1' \\ u_2' \end{bmatrix} + \begin{bmatrix} 1 \\ 0 \end{bmatrix} x, \tag{7.41}$$

or

$$\dot{\mathbf{u}}' = \mathbf{A}'\mathbf{u}' + \mathbf{g}x. \tag{7.42}$$

From equation (7.27),

$$\mathbf{y}' = \begin{bmatrix} y_0' \\ y_1' \end{bmatrix} = \begin{bmatrix} 1 \\ 2 \end{bmatrix} u_1', \tag{7.43}$$

or the approximate first-order equations for y_0' and y_1' can be written

$$\dot{y}_0' = -(1 + 2/5e^{-t})y_0' + x \tag{7.44}$$

and

$$\dot{y}_1' = -(1 + 2/5e^{-t})y_1' + 2x. \tag{7.45}$$

To investigate in more detail the value of this approximation, the $\mathbf{G}'$ matrix is determined through equations (7.23), (7.37), and (7.38) as

$$\mathbf{G}' = \begin{bmatrix} -(3 + 2/5e^{-t}) & 1 \\ -(2 + 4/5e^{-t}) & 0 \end{bmatrix}. \tag{7.46}$$

The equation which approximates equation (7.28) can then be written as

$$\begin{bmatrix} \dot{y}_0' \\ \dot{y}_1' \end{bmatrix} = \begin{bmatrix} -(3 + 2/5e^{-t}) & 1 \\ -(2 + 4/5e^{-t}) & 0 \end{bmatrix}\begin{bmatrix} y_0' \\ y_1' \end{bmatrix} + \begin{bmatrix} 1 \\ 2 \end{bmatrix} x. \tag{7.47}$$

The error in the solution of the approximate equation is then given by

$$\begin{bmatrix} \epsilon_0' \\ \epsilon_1' \end{bmatrix} = \begin{bmatrix} y_0 - y_0' \\ y_1 - y_1' \end{bmatrix}, \tag{7.48}$$

which is examined in Appendix VI by examining a bound on the error.

INCREASING THE ORDERS OF THE INTEGRAL
AND DIFFERENTIAL OPERATORS

The approximation problem discussed in this section can be stated as follows: Let W be a differential equation of the form

$$\sum_{i=0}^{n} a_i(t) \frac{d^i y}{dt^i} = \sum_{i=0}^{m} b_i(t) \frac{d^i x}{dt^i} \, . \tag{7.49}$$

Suppose that W produces a desirable response when subjected to a particular input $x(t)$. Suppose, however, that in view of practical considerations this equation is not acceptable because the difference in the orders of the integral and differential operators is too small; that is,

$$n - m < N, \tag{7.50}$$

where N is the required order difference. For instance, suppose

$$n - m = N - b, \tag{7.51}$$

where b is a positive integer. The problem then is: How can an equation

$$\sum_{i=i}^{n+b+q} a_i'(t) \frac{d^i y'}{dt^i} = \sum_{i=0}^{m+q} b_i'(t) \frac{d^i x}{dt^i} \tag{7.52}$$

be simply and quickly formed, so that, for the same input $x(t)$, it produces an output $y'(t)$ that very closely approximates $y(t)$, the desired output of equation (7.49)? The proposed method for solving this problem

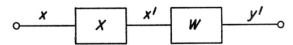

Figure 7.1. Approximation of differential equation W.

is indicated in figure 7.1. A differential equation, whose difference in order of integral and differential operators is b, is to be cascaded with W, thus forming an overall differential equation W', given by

$$W' = WX \tag{7.53}$$

that has the proper order difference N. The properties of X are to be such that the difference between x and x' is kept at a small value at all times. In particular, it shall be required that the difference ϵ between x and x', that is,

$$\epsilon = x - x', \tag{7.54}$$

shall approach zero asymptotically. It will be seen that the rate of approach can be controlled by proper choice of the characteristic equation of the differential equation which describes the error.

Let the differential equation X be given in the form

$$\sum_{i=0}^{b+q} \alpha_i(t) \frac{d^i x'}{dt^i} = \sum_{i=0}^{q} \beta_i(t) \frac{d^i x}{dt^i} . \tag{7.55}$$

The $\alpha_i(t)$ are first chosen as constants. Their choice is discussed below. After they have been chosen, the operator

$$\sum_{i=0}^{b+q} \alpha_i \frac{d^i}{dt^i} \tag{7.56}$$

is applied to both sides of equation (7.54), thus forming the equation

$$\sum_{i=0}^{b+q} \alpha_i \frac{d^i \epsilon}{dt^i} = \sum_{i=0}^{b+q} \alpha_i \frac{d^i x}{dt^i} - \sum_{i=0}^{b+q} \alpha_i \frac{d^i x'}{dt^i} . \tag{7.57}$$

Substituting equation (7.55) into (7.57), the differential equation for the difference ϵ becomes

$$\sum_{i=0}^{b+q} \alpha_i \frac{d^i \epsilon}{dt^i} = \sum_{i=q+1}^{b+q} \alpha_i \frac{d^i x}{dt^i} + \sum_{i=0}^{q} (\alpha_i - \beta_i) \frac{d^i x}{dt^i} . \tag{7.58}$$

Now if ϵ is required to approach zero asymptotically, then, in addition to the equation being stable, the right-hand side of equation (7.58) must be zero; that is, the β_i must be chosen such that

$$\sum_{i=q+1}^{b+q} \alpha_i \frac{d^i x}{dt^i} + \sum_{i=0}^{q} (\alpha_i - \beta_i) \frac{d^i x}{dt^i} = 0. \tag{7.59}$$

The method of choosing the $\beta_i(t)$ will depend in general upon the form of $x(t)$. To illustrate this method, three forms of inputs will be examined.

Polynomial Inputs

Suppose

$$x(t) = \sum_{j=0}^{q} c_i t^i, \tag{7.60}$$

where the c_i are real constants. It is apparent that

$$\frac{d^i x}{dt^i} = 0, \qquad i = q + 1, q + 2, \cdots, q + b;$$

therefore equation (7.59) reduces to

$$\sum_{i=0}^{q} (\alpha_i - \beta_i) \frac{d^i x}{dt^i} = 0, \qquad (7.61)$$

and the obvious solution for β_i to satisfy this equation is

$$\beta_i = \alpha_i. \qquad (7.62)$$

Inspection of equation (7.62) indicates that q is chosen as the highest power of the polynomial input and also that the β_i are constants since the α_i were chosen as constants. The resulting equation X [equation (7.55)] is then time-invariant.

Exponential Inputs

Suppose

$$x(t) = \sum_{j=0}^{q} c_j e^{\gamma_j t}, \qquad (7.63)$$

where the c_j are real constants and the γ_j are, in general, complex numbers. In order to maintain $x(t)$ real, it is necessary that the complex γ_j occur in complex conjugate pairs.

If equation (7.63) is substituted into equation (7.59), the following equation is formed:

$$\sum_{i=q+1}^{b+q} \alpha_i \sum_{j=0}^{q} c_j \frac{d^i e^{\gamma_j t}}{dt^i} + \sum_{i=0}^{q} (\alpha_i - \beta_i) \sum_{j=0}^{q} c_j \frac{d^i e^{\gamma_j t}}{dt^i} = 0, \qquad (7.64)$$

or

$$\sum_{i=q+1}^{b+q} \sum_{j=0}^{q} \alpha_i c_j \gamma_j^i e^{\gamma_j t} + \sum_{i=0}^{q} \sum_{j=0}^{q} (\alpha_i - \beta_i) c_j \gamma_j^i e^{\gamma_j t} = 0. \qquad (7.65)$$

Equation (7.65) can be rewritten

$$\sum_{j=0}^{q} c_j e^{\gamma_j t} \left\{ \sum_{i=q+1}^{b+q} \alpha_i \gamma_j^i + \sum_{i=0}^{q} (\alpha_i - \beta_i) \gamma_j^i \right\} = 0. \qquad (7.66)$$

The β_i are then chosen to satisfy the set of simultaneous equations

$$\sum_{i=q+1}^{b+q} \alpha_i \gamma_j^i + \sum_{i=0}^{q} (\alpha_i - \beta_i) \gamma_j^i = 0, \qquad j = 0, 1, \cdots, n. \qquad (7.67)$$

Note that by choosing the highest nonzero β_i to be β_q, equation (7.67) produces exactly $q + 1$ equations in $q + 1$ unknowns. It should be noted that, since the α_i and γ_j are constants, the β_i are constants; hence the resulting equation X is time-invariant.

General Inputs

Suppose that the input is a general function $cx(t)$, where c is a constant and $x(t)$ has at least b continuous derivatives. In equation (7.59), if q is made equal to zero then the equation can be rewritten

$$\sum_{i=1}^{b} \alpha_i \frac{d^i cx}{dt^i} + (\alpha_0 - \beta_0)cx = 0 , \qquad (7.68)$$

or

$$c \left\{ \sum_{i=1}^{b} \alpha_i \frac{d^i x}{dt^i} + \alpha_0 x - \beta_0 x \right\} = 0; \qquad (7.69)$$

therefore

$$\beta_0 = \alpha_0 + \frac{1}{x} \left\{ \sum_{i=1}^{b} \alpha_i \frac{d^i x}{dt^i} \right\}. \qquad (7.70)$$

The function β_0 is, in general, a function of time, and this result obviously produces an X which is time-variable. Because of the division by x, it might be impractical to use the result in (7.70) in many common situations. It will usually be desirable to approximate inputs by exponentials or polynomials and apply the results in equations (7.67) or (7.62), respectively.

Once the β_i's have been chosen such that equation (7.59) is satisfied, the equation for the error [equation (7.58)] becomes

$$\sum_{i=0}^{b+q} \alpha_i \frac{d^i \epsilon}{dt^i} = 0. \qquad (7.71)$$

Equation (7.71) represents a constant-coefficient, homogeneous differential equation whose solution is the error. Earlier it was stated that the α_i are chosen first. The choice of the α_i is now more readily apparent. They are chosen such that the error ϵ approaches zero rapidly enough so that the difference between x and x' will not make the output y' of W differ appreciably from the desired output y. The choice of the α_i, then, will require some knowledge of the solution of the differential equation W.

APPENDIXES

Appendix I

DETERMINATION OF A DIFFERENTIAL EQUATION FROM A WEIGHTING FUNCTION

The weighting function of a physically realizable linear system can be defined as a function $W(t, \tau)$ such that if an input $x(t)$ is applied to the system, the output $y(t)$ is given by the convolution integral

$$y(t) = \int_{-\infty}^{t} W(t, \theta)x(\theta) \, d\theta. \tag{I.1}$$

The upper limit of the integral must be t, since the physical realizability of the system requires that

$$W(t, \tau) = 0 \qquad \text{for} \qquad \tau > t. \tag{I.2}$$

If the system for which $W(t, \tau)$ is the weighting function can be described exactly by an nth-order ordinary linear differential equation, then the weighting function $W(t, \tau)$ has the form

$$W(t, \tau) = \sum_{i=1}^{n} \alpha_i(\tau)q_i(t) + F_0(t)\delta(t - \tau), \tag{I.3}$$

or

$$W(t, \tau) = W_1(t, \tau) + F_0(t)\delta(t - \tau), \tag{I.3a}$$

where the $\alpha_i(\tau)$ are linearly independent functions of τ, and the $q_i(t)$ are linearly independent functions of t. The $q_i(t)$ are also linearly independent solutions of the homogeneous part of the differential equation. The term $F_0(t)\delta(t - \tau)$ indicates that a portion of the input may merely be multiplied by a factor $F_0(t)$ as it passes through the system.

Assume now that a weighting function of the form in equation (I.3)

89

has been generated and it is desired to determine the differential equation to which it corresponds. Since there are n independent solutions $q_i(t)$ in $W(t, \tau)$, the order of the differential equation must be n, and it is assumed that it has the form

$$\sum_{j=0}^{n} a_j(t) \frac{d^j y}{dt^j} = \sum_{j=0}^{n} b_j(t) \frac{d^j x}{dt^j},\tag{I.4}$$

where the $a_j(t)$ and $b_j(t)$ are to be determined.

Since the $q_i(t)$ are solutions of the homogeneous part of equation (I.4), it follows that

$$\sum_{j=0}^{n} a_j(t) \frac{d^j q_i}{dt^j} = 0,\qquad i = 1, 2, \cdots, n.\tag{I.5}$$

Equations (I.5) represent n simultaneous equations in the $n + 1$ unknown $a_j(t)$. If $a_n(t)$ is chosen to be unity, these equations can be solved for the remaining $a_j(t)$.

Once the $a_j(t)$ are known, the $b_j(t)$ can be determined. Suppose that the weighting function which corresponds to the homogeneous portion of equation (I.4), that is, the solution to the following problem, were known:

$$\sum_{j=0}^{n} a_j(t) \frac{\partial^j G(t, \tau)}{\partial t^j} = 0,$$

$$\frac{\partial^j G(t, \tau)}{\partial t^j}\bigg|_{t=\tau} = 0,\qquad j = 0, 1, \cdots, n - 2,\tag{I.6}$$

$$\frac{\partial^{n-1} G(t, \tau)}{\partial t^{n-1}} = 1.$$

If $G(t, \tau)$ is known, then the solution to equation (I.4) can be written

$$y(t) = \int_{-\infty}^{t} G(t, \theta) \left[\sum_{j=0}^{n} b_j(\theta) \frac{d^j x(\theta)}{d\theta^j} \right] d\theta.\tag{I.7}$$

Then by virtue of equation (I.1),

$$\int_{-\infty}^{t} G(t, \theta) \left[\sum_{j=0}^{n} b_j(\theta) \frac{d^j x(\theta)}{d\theta^j} \right] d\theta = \int_{-\infty}^{t} W(t, \theta) x(\theta) \, d\theta.\tag{I.8}$$

Now if the differential operator

$$\sum_{p=0}^{n} a_p(t) \frac{d^p}{dt^p}\tag{I.9}$$

is applied to both sides of equation (I.9), the equation

$$\sum_{j=0}^{n} b_j(t) \frac{d^j x}{dt^j} = \sum_{p=0}^{n} a_p(t) \frac{d^p}{dt^p} \left\{ \int_{-\infty}^{t} W(t, \theta) x(\theta) \, d\theta \right\} \tag{I.10}$$

is formed. Now let equation (I.3a) be substituted into equation (I.10), and for simplification of notation, let

$$F_i(t) = \frac{\partial^{i-1} W_1(t, \tau)}{\partial t^{i-1}} \bigg|_{\tau \to t^-} = \frac{\partial^{i-1} W(t, \tau)}{\partial t^{i-1}} \bigg|_{\tau \to t^-}. \tag{I.11}$$

Then the derivatives in equation (I.10) are given by

$$\frac{d^p}{dt^p} \left\{ \int_{-\infty}^{t} W(t, \theta) x(\theta) \, d\theta \right\} = \int_{-\infty}^{t} \frac{\partial^p}{\partial t^p} [W_1(t, \theta)] x(\theta) \, d\theta$$

$$+ \sum_{k=0}^{p} \frac{d^k}{dt^k} [F_{p-k}(t) x(t)],$$

$$p = 0, 1, \cdots, n. \tag{I.12}$$

The right-hand side of equation (I.10) can, consequently, be given by

$$\sum_{p=0}^{n} a_p(t) \int_{-\infty}^{t} \frac{\partial^p}{\partial t^p} [W_1(t, \theta)] x(\theta) \, d\theta$$

$$+ \sum_{p=0}^{n} a_p(t) \sum_{k=0}^{p} \frac{d^k}{dt^k} [F_{p-k}(t) x(t)]. \tag{I.13}$$

Since

$$\sum_{p=0}^{n} \int_{-\infty}^{t} a_p(t) \frac{\partial^p}{\partial t^p} [W_1(t, \theta)] x(\theta) \, d\theta = 0, \tag{I.14}$$

and

$$\frac{d^k}{dt^k} [F_{p-k}(t) x(t)] = \sum_{j=0}^{k} \binom{k}{j} \frac{d^{k-j}}{dt^{k-j}} [F_{p-k}(t)] \frac{d^j x}{dt^j}, \tag{I.15}$$

it follows that

$$\sum_{j=0}^{n} b_j(t) \frac{d^j x}{dt^j} = \sum_{p=0}^{n} \sum_{k=0}^{p} \sum_{j=0}^{k} \binom{k}{j} a_p(t) \frac{d^{k-j}}{dt^{k-j}} [F_{p-k}(t)] \frac{d^j x}{dt^j}. \tag{I.16}$$

Now if the summations on the right-hand side of equation (I.16) are rearranged as follows:

$$\sum_{p=0}^{n} \sum_{k=0}^{p} \sum_{j=0}^{k} = \sum_{p=0}^{n} \sum_{j=0}^{p} \sum_{k=j}^{p} = \sum_{j=0}^{n} \sum_{p=j}^{n} \sum_{k=j}^{p}, \tag{I.17}$$

then it follows that

$$b_j(t) = \sum_{p=j}^{n} \sum_{k=j}^{p} \binom{k}{j} a_p(t) \frac{d^{k-j}[F_{p-k}(t)]}{dt^{k-j}},$$

$$j = 0, 1, 2, \cdots, n. \qquad (I.18)$$

Equations (I.18) then allow the $b_j(t)$ to be determined in terms of the $a_p(t)$ and the $F_i(t)$.

A word about differentiability of the $\alpha_i(\tau)$ and the $q_i(t)$ in the weighting function $W(t, \tau)$ is in order at this point. From the definition of the $F_i(t)$ in equation (I.11), and from equation (I.18), it can be seen that in order for the $b_j(t)$ to be continuous functions of time, the $q_i(t)$ should have $2n$ continuous derivatives and the $\alpha_i(\tau)$ and $F_0(t)$ should have n continuous derivatives.

Appendix II

The development in chapters 6 and 7 assumed that a differential equation of the form

$$\sum_{i=0}^{n} a_i(t) \frac{d^i y}{dt^i} = \sum_{i=0}^{n} b_i(t) \frac{d^i x}{dt^i} \tag{II.1}$$

can be rewritten in the form of an equivalent set of n first-order differential equations. There are several forms that these equations might take [16], [22]; however, only that one which the author found most useful from the standpoint of simplicity is presented in this appendix. The development contained herein is that of Matyash [19] with some slight changes that are convenient to the developments in this monograph.

To simplify the notation in equation (II.1), let

$$L = \sum_{i=0}^{n} a_i(t) \frac{d^i}{dt^i} \quad \text{and} \quad M = \sum_{i=0}^{n} b_i(t) \frac{d^i}{dt^i} . \tag{II.2}$$

Then equation (II.1) can be written

$$L(y) = M(x). \tag{II.3}$$

Now let two subsidiary operators be defined by

$$L_1 = \sum_{i=0}^{n} \alpha_i(t) \frac{d^i}{dt^i} \tag{II.4}$$

and

$$M_1 = \sum_{i=0}^{n} \beta_i(t) \frac{d^i}{dt^i} , \tag{II.5}$$

where $\alpha_i(t)$ and $\beta_i(t)$ are defined in (II.10) and (II.11).

Now assume that the following set of equations is valid:

$$y_0 = -\alpha_n y - \beta_n x, \tag{II.6}$$

$$-\dot{y}_{k-1} = y_k + \alpha_{n-k} y + \beta_{n-k} x, \qquad k = 1, 2, \cdots, n-1, \tag{II.7}$$

$$-\dot{y}_{n-1} = \alpha_0 y + \beta_0 x. \tag{II.8}$$

Then if y_0 from equation (II.6) is substituted into (II.7) for $k = 1$, and, in the resulting equation, y_1 is determined and substituted into equation (II.7) for $k = 2$, and so on, all of the y_i are eliminated and equation (II.8) becomes an nth-order differential equation in y, which is given by

$$\sum_{i=0}^{n} (-1)^i \frac{d^i[\alpha_i y]}{dt^i} = -\sum_{i=0}^{n} (-1)^i \frac{d^i[\beta_i x]}{dt^i}. \tag{II.9}$$

Now if the adjoint operators of L_1 and M_1 are denoted L_1^* and M_1^*, respectively, that is,

$$L_1^*(y) = \sum_{i=0}^{n} (-1)^i (\alpha_i y)^{(i)} \tag{II.10}$$

and

$$M_1^*(x) = \sum_{i=0}^{n} (-1)^i (\beta_i x)^{(i)}, \tag{II.11}$$

then equation (II.9) can be written

$$L_1^*(y) = -M_1^*(x); \tag{II.12}$$

and if now equations (II.1) and (II.9) are made identical,

$$L_1^*(y) = L(y) \quad \text{and} \quad -M_1^*(x) = M(x), \tag{II.13}$$

then since

$$(K^*)^* = K,$$

K being any linear differential operator, equations (II.13) can be written

$$L_1(y) = L^*(y) \quad \text{and} \quad M_1(x) = -M^*(x). \tag{II.14}$$

In other words, the α's and β's of the n first-order differential equations in (II.6), (II.7), and (II.8) are determined from the adjoint operators L^* and M^*.

A further refinement which can be made is the following: Make $a_n(t) \equiv 1$ (without loss of generality); then

$$\alpha_n \equiv (-1)^n,$$

and from (II.6),

$$y = (-1)^{n+1}[y_0 + \beta_n x]. \tag{II.15}$$

Substituting this relationship for y into equations (II.7), the final form of the n first-order equations becomes

$$\dot{y}_0 = (-1)^n \alpha_{n-1} y_0 - y_1 - [\beta_{n-1} + (-1)^{n+1}\beta_n \alpha_{n-1}]x,$$

$$\dot{y}_1 = (-1)^n \alpha_{n-2} y_0 - y_2 - [\beta_{n-2} + (-1)^{n+1}\beta_n \alpha_{n-2}]x,$$

$$\cdot\ \cdot \tag{II.16}$$

$$\dot{y}_{n-2} = (-1)^n \alpha_1 y_0 - y_{n-1} - [\beta_1 + (-1)^{n+1}\beta_n \alpha_1]x,$$

$$\dot{y}_{n-1} = (-1)^n \alpha_0 y_0 - [\beta_0 + (-1)^{n+1}\beta_n \alpha_0]x.$$

Appendix III

SYNTHESIS OF TIME-VARIABLE
DIFFERENTIAL EQUATIONS WITH
ANALOG COMPUTER ELEMENTS

One of the advantages of determining the compensation network of a linear control in the form of a differential equation is that in differential-equation form the compensation network can readily be built. In particular, if the networks are time-variable, they can be built with analog computer elements [19].

The types of differential equations which must be synthesized will have the form

$$\sum_{i=0}^{n} a_i(t) \frac{d^i y}{dt^i} = \sum_{i=0}^{n} b_i(t) \frac{d^i x}{dt^i} \; . \tag{III.1}$$

The only problem which arises in synthesizing equation (III.1) is how to handle the right-hand side, which contains derivatives of the input x. This problem is circumvented by writing equation (III.1) in an equivalent vector form

$$\dot{\mathbf{y}} = \mathbf{A}\mathbf{y} + \mathbf{f}x, \tag{III.2}$$

where $\mathbf{y}$ is an n-vector. The solution of equation (III.1), $y(t)$, is then given by

$$y(t) = \mathbf{c}^T \mathbf{y} + rx, \tag{III.3}$$

where $\mathbf{c}$ is an n-vector and r is a scalar that are determined by the relationship between equations (III.1) and (III.3). In Appendix II it was shown how equation (III.1) can be written in vector form as in equation (III.2). Equations (II.16) represent a formulation for equation (III.2), and equation (II.15) represents a formulation for equation (III.3).

Equations (II.15) and (II.16) can be synthesized by analog computer elements in the form shown in figure III.1, *a*.

96

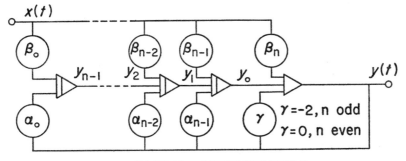

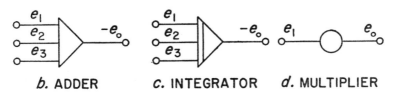

a. GENERAL CONFIGURATION

b. ADDER   *c.* INTEGRATOR   *d.* MULTIPLIER

Figure III.1. Analog computer schematic of equations (II.15) and (II.16).

The symbols used in figure III.1, *a*, are defined in figures III.1, *b*, III.1, *c*, and III.1, *d*. In figure III.1, *b*, the output of an adder e_0 is given by

$$e_0 = -(e_1 + e_2 + e_3). \tag{III.4}$$

In figure III.1, *c*, the output of an integrator e_0 is given by

$$e_0 = -\int^t (e_1 + e_2 + e_3) \, dt. \tag{III.5}$$

In figure III.1, *d*, the output of a multiplier is given by

$$e_0 = a(t)e_1. \tag{III.6}$$

The advantage of synthesizing equations (II.15) and (II.16) instead of equation (III.1) is that in the former, differentiations are not required.

Appendix IV

A USEFUL IDENTITY

The following identity is useful in working with a noncommutative algebra of linear transformations in control systems applications:

$$GK[I \pm HGK]^{-1} = [I \pm GKH]^{-1}GK. \qquad (\text{IV}.1)$$

Proof:

$$
\begin{aligned}
GK[I \pm HGK]^{-1} &= GK\{(GK)^{-1}GK \pm HGK\}^{-1} \\
&= GK\{[(GK)^{-1} \pm H]GK\}^{-1} \\
&= (GK)(GK)^{-1}[(GK)^{-1} \pm H]^{-1} \\
&= \{(GK)^{-1} \pm H\}^{-1} \\
&= \{(GK)^{-1} \pm (GK)^{-1}GKH\}^{-1} \\
&= \{(GK)^{-1}[I \pm GKH]\}^{-1} \\
&= [I \pm GKH]^{-1}GK. \qquad \text{Q.E.D.}
\end{aligned}
$$

From equation (IV.1) the following identities are immediately apparent:

$$GK[I \pm GK]^{-1} = [I \pm GK]^{-1}GK, \qquad (\text{IV}.2)$$

$$G(I \pm G)^{-1} = (I \pm G)G. \qquad (\text{IV}.3)$$

Appendix V

BEST LEAST-SQUARES APPROXIMATE
SOLUTIONS OF INCOMPATIBLE
SIMULTANEOUS ALGEBRAIC EQUATIONS

Consider the problem of finding a solution to the following equations:

$$c_1 \gamma_1 + c_2 \gamma_2 + \cdots + c_m \gamma_m = \gamma_0, \qquad (V.1)$$

where the c_i are unknown scalar qualities and $\gamma_1, \gamma_2, \cdots, \gamma_m$ are known, linearly independent n-dimensional column vectors. Suppose that $n > m$; then, unless $\gamma_0 (\gamma_0 \neq 0)$ belongs to the subspace G spanned by $\gamma_1, \cdots, \gamma_m$, there is no solution for the c_i in equation (V.1).

If there is no solution, then the problem may be to find the best (in some sense) approximate solution to (V.1). It will be assumed that the best approximate solution for the c_i is that solution which minimizes the square of the magnitude of the vector difference between γ_0 and $\sum_{i=1}^{m} c_i \gamma_i$. The best approximation of γ_0 in the subspace then will be the projection of γ_0 onto the subspace G. The error vector, given by

$$\varepsilon = \sum_{i=1}^{m} c_i \gamma_i - \gamma_0, \qquad (V.2)$$

or, in matrix notation,

$$\varepsilon = \Gamma c - \gamma_0, \qquad (V.3)$$

where

$$c = \begin{bmatrix} c_1 \\ \vdots \\ c_m \end{bmatrix} \quad \text{and} \quad \Gamma = [\gamma_1, \cdots, \gamma_m],$$

is orthogonal to each vector γ_i; therefore the inner product of ε and each γ_i must be zero; that is,

$$\gamma_i^T \varepsilon = 0, \qquad i = 1, 2, \cdots, m, \tag{V.4}$$

where γ_i^T is the transpose of the vector γ_i. Equations (V.4) can be written in the matrix form

$$\Gamma^T \varepsilon = 0, \tag{V.5}$$

where Γ^T is the transpose of Γ. If equation (V.3) is substituted into equation (V.5), the matrix equation

$$\Gamma^T \Gamma c - \Gamma^T \gamma_0 = 0 \tag{V.6}$$

is formed. The best solution for c is then given by

$$c = (\Gamma^T \Gamma)^{-1} \Gamma^T \gamma_0. \tag{V.7}$$

Appendix VI

A BOUND ON THE ERRORS
OF APPROXIMATE SYSTEMS

In the course of developing an approximation to a given differential equation, it is necessary to examine the difference between the outputs of the given differential equation and its approximation for a particular input. From this difference, or error, some measure of the value of the approximation can be attained.

Let the given differential equation be given by

$$\dot{\mathbf{y}} = \mathbf{G}\mathbf{y} + \mathbf{f}x, \tag{VI.1}$$

and let the approximation of equation (VI.1) be

$$\dot{\mathbf{y}}_1 = \mathbf{G}_1\mathbf{y}_1 + \mathbf{f}_1x. \tag{VI.2}$$

These two equations are assumed to have the same order and are, in general, both time-variable.

The difference between equations (VI.1) and (VI.2) can be written

$$(\dot{\mathbf{y}} - \dot{\mathbf{y}}_1) = \mathbf{G}\mathbf{y} - \mathbf{G}_1\mathbf{y}_1 + (\mathbf{f} - \mathbf{f}_1)x + (\mathbf{G}_1\mathbf{y} - \mathbf{G}_1\mathbf{y}); \tag{VI.3}$$

or, letting $\varepsilon = \mathbf{y} - \mathbf{y}_1$,

$$\dot{\varepsilon} = \mathbf{G}_1\varepsilon + (\mathbf{G} - \mathbf{G}_1)\mathbf{y} + (\mathbf{f} - \mathbf{f}_1)x. \tag{VI.4}$$

Now let

$$\mathbf{B} = \mathbf{G} - \mathbf{G}_1, \tag{VI.5}$$

and

$$\mathbf{b} = \mathbf{f} - \mathbf{f}_1;$$

then equation (VI.4) becomes

$$\dot{\varepsilon} = \mathbf{G}_1\varepsilon + \mathbf{B}\mathbf{y} + \mathbf{b}x. \tag{VI.6}$$

If the solution of equation (VI.6) can be obtained explicitly, the problem is solved. In general, however, an explicit solution for equation (VI.6) will be difficult to obtain, in which case three alternate courses are open:

1. A computer solution can be obtained.
2. An approximate solution might be obtained.
3. Some bound on the error vector ε might be obtained.

In this appendix, the third course is explored and a bound on a particular norm of the error vector is obtained. This bound is limited in its use, but in many cases it may provide a simple check on the worth of an approximation.

The norm which is used in this development is defined as follows: If $\mathbf{A}$ is a matrix, then its norm is given by

$$\text{norm} \quad \mathbf{A} = \|\mathbf{A}\| = (\text{trace} \quad \mathbf{A}\mathbf{A}^T)^{\frac{1}{2}}, \tag{VI.7}$$

where $\mathbf{A}^T$ is the transpose of the $\mathbf{A}$ matrix. The norm of the error vector ε, by virtue of equation (VI.7), is the square root of the sum of the squares of its components.

If $\mathbf{W}_1(t, \tau)$ is defined as the weighting-function matrix of the homogeneous differential equation

$$\dot{\mathbf{u}} = \mathbf{G}_1\mathbf{u}, \tag{VI.8}$$

then the solution of equation (VI.6) is given by

$$\varepsilon(t) = \int_\tau^t \mathbf{W}_1(t, \theta)\mathbf{B}(\theta)\mathbf{y}(\theta) \, d\theta + \int_\tau^t \mathbf{W}_1(t, \theta)\mathbf{b}(\theta)x(\theta) \, d\theta. \tag{VI.9}$$

Then

$$\|\varepsilon(t)\| \leqq \left\| \int_\tau^t \mathbf{W}_1(t, \theta)\mathbf{B}(\theta)\mathbf{y}(\theta) \, d\theta \right\|$$

$$+ \left\| \int_\tau^t \mathbf{W}_1(t, \theta)\mathbf{b}(\theta)x(\theta) \, d\theta \right\|$$

$$\leqq \int_\tau^t \|\mathbf{W}_1(t, \theta)\mathbf{B}(\theta)\mathbf{y}(\theta)\| \, d\theta$$

$$+ \int_\tau^t \|\mathbf{W}_1(t, \theta)\mathbf{b}(\theta)x(\theta)\| \, d\theta \tag{VI.10}$$

$$\leqq \int_\tau^t \|\mathbf{W}_1(t, \theta)\| \, \|\mathbf{B}(\theta)\| \, \|\mathbf{y}(\theta)\| \, d\theta$$

$$+ \int_\tau^t \|\mathbf{W}_1(t, \theta)\| \, \|\mathbf{b}(\theta)\| \, \|x(\theta)\| \, d\theta.$$

If

$$M_y = \max \|\mathbf{y}(\theta)\|,$$
$$M_x = \max \|x(\theta)\| = \max |x(\theta)|, \tag{VI.11}$$

then

$$\|\boldsymbol{\epsilon}(t)\| \leqq M_y \int_\tau^t \|\mathbf{W}_1(t, \theta)\| \, \|\mathbf{B}(\theta)\| \, d\theta$$

$$+ M_x \int_\tau^t \|\mathbf{W}_1(t, \theta)\| \, \|\mathbf{b}(\theta)\| \, d\theta. \tag{VI.12}$$

Now let

$$\mathbf{G}_1 = \mathbf{A} + \mathbf{C}(t), \tag{VI.13}$$

where $\mathbf{A}$ is a constant nonsingular matrix and $\mathbf{C}(t)$ is a time-variable matrix. The eigenvalues of $\mathbf{A}$ have negative real parts.

Since $\mathbf{W}_1(t, \theta)$ is the weighting function of equation (VI.8), then it must satisfy the equation

$$\frac{\partial}{\partial t} [\mathbf{W}_1(t, \theta)] = \mathbf{A}\mathbf{W}_1(t, \theta) + \mathbf{C}(t)\mathbf{W}_1(t,\theta), \tag{VI.14}$$

where $\mathbf{W}_1(\theta, \theta) = \mathbf{I}$ (the identity matrix).
Consequently,

$$\mathbf{W}_1(t, \theta) = \mathbf{W}(t - \theta) + \int_\theta^t \mathbf{W}(t - \alpha)\mathbf{C}(\alpha)\mathbf{W}_1(\alpha, \theta) \, d\alpha, \tag{VI.15}$$

where $W(t - \theta)$ satisfies the equation

$$\frac{\partial}{\partial t} [\mathbf{W}(t - \theta)] = \mathbf{A}\mathbf{W}(t - \theta), \quad \text{where} \quad \mathbf{W}(\theta - \theta) = \mathbf{I}. \tag{VI.16}$$

Now if the eigenvalues of $\mathbf{A}$ all have negative real parts, then $\|\mathbf{W}(t - \theta)\|$ can be bounded by an exponential [4]; that is,

$$\|\mathbf{W}(t - \theta)\| \leqq c_1 e^{-a(t-\theta)}, \tag{VI.17}$$

where c_1 and a are positive real constants. Then, from equations (VI.15) and (VI.17),

$$\|\mathbf{W}_1(t, \theta)\| \leqq c_1 e^{-a(t-\theta)}$$

$$+ \int_\theta^t c_1 e^{-a(t-\alpha)} \|\mathbf{C}(\alpha)\| \, \|\mathbf{W}_1(\alpha, \theta)\| \, d\alpha. \tag{VI.18}$$

Thus

$$\left\|\mathbf{W}_1(t,\,\theta)\right\|e^{at} \leqq c_1 e^{a\theta} + \int_\theta^t c_1 e^{a\alpha} \left\|\mathbf{C}(\alpha)\right\| \left\|\mathbf{W}_1(\alpha,\,\theta)\right\| d\alpha, \quad \text{(VI.19)}$$

whence

$$c_1 \left\|\mathbf{C}(t)\right\| \left\|\mathbf{W}_1(t,\,\theta)\right\|e^{at}$$

$$\leqq c_1 \left\|\mathbf{C}(t)\right\|\left[c_1 e^{a\theta} + \int_\theta^t c_1 e^{a\alpha} \left\|\mathbf{C}(\alpha)\right\| \left\|\mathbf{W}_1(\alpha,\,\theta)\right\| d\alpha\right], \quad \text{(VI.20)}$$

and

$$\frac{c_1 \left\|\mathbf{C}(t)\right\| \left\|\mathbf{W}_1(t,\,\theta)\right\|e^{at}}{c_1 e^{a\theta} + \int_\theta^t c_1 \left\|\mathbf{C}(\alpha)\right\| \left\|\mathbf{W}_1(\alpha,\,\theta)\right\|e^{a\alpha}d\alpha} \leqq c_1 \left\|\mathbf{C}(t)\right\|. \quad \text{(VI.21)}$$

Integrating inequality (VI.21) forms

$$\log\left[c_1 e^{a\theta} + \int_\theta^t c_1 \left\|\mathbf{C}(\alpha)\right\| \left\|\mathbf{W}_1(\alpha,\,\theta)\right\|e^{a\alpha}\,d\alpha\right] - \log c_1 e^{a\theta}$$

$$\leqq \int_\theta^t c_1 \left\|\mathbf{C}(\alpha)\right\|\,d\alpha, \quad \text{(VI.22)}$$

and

$$\frac{c_1 e^{a\theta} + \int_\theta^t c_1 \left\|\mathbf{C}(\alpha)\right\| \left\|\mathbf{W}_1(\alpha,\,\theta)\right\|e^{a\alpha}d\alpha}{c_1 e^{a\theta}} \leqq \exp\int_\theta^t c_1 \left\|\mathbf{C}(\alpha)\right\|d\alpha. \quad \text{(VI.23)}$$

Finally, from equation (VI.19) and (VI.23)

$$\left\|\mathbf{W}_1(t,\,\theta)\right\| \leqq c_1 \exp\left\{-a(t-\theta) + \int_\theta^t c_1 \left\|\mathbf{C}(\alpha)\right\|d\alpha\right\} \quad \text{(VI.24)}$$

Then from equations (VI.24) and (VI.12)

$$\left\|\boldsymbol{\varepsilon}(t)\right\| \leqq \int_\tau^t c_1 \exp\left\{-a(t-\theta) + \int_\theta^t c_1 \left\|\mathbf{C}(\alpha)\right\|d\alpha\right\}$$

$$\cdot \left\{M_y \left\|\mathbf{B}(\theta)\right\| + M_x \left\|\mathbf{b}(\theta)\right\|\right\}d\theta. \quad \text{(VI.25)}$$

For the special case when (VI.6) is time-invariant, $\left\|\mathbf{C}(\alpha)\right\| = 0$, and $\left\|\mathbf{B}(\theta)\right\|$ and $\left\|\mathbf{b}(\theta)\right\|$ are both constant, equation (VI.25) reduces to

$$\left\|\boldsymbol{\varepsilon}(t)\right\| \leqq \frac{c_1}{a}\left\{M_y \left\|\mathbf{B}\right\| + M_x \left\|\mathbf{b}\right\|\right\}\left[1 - e^{-a(t-\tau)}\right]. \quad \text{(VI.26)}$$

EXAMPLE

In the example in chapter 6, the equation

$$\begin{bmatrix} \dot{y}_0 \\ \dot{y}_1 \end{bmatrix} = \begin{bmatrix} -3 & 1 \\ -(2+e^{-t}) & 0 \end{bmatrix} \begin{bmatrix} y_0 \\ y_1 \end{bmatrix} + \begin{bmatrix} 1 \\ 2 \end{bmatrix} x \tag{VI.27}$$

was approximated by

$$\begin{bmatrix} \dot{y}_0' \\ \dot{y}_1' \end{bmatrix} = \begin{bmatrix} -(3+2/5e^{-t}) & 1 \\ -(2+4/5e^{-t}) & 0 \end{bmatrix} \begin{bmatrix} y_0' \\ y_1' \end{bmatrix} + \begin{bmatrix} 1 \\ 2 \end{bmatrix} x. \tag{VI.28}$$

Using equation (VI.25), the error bound will be found for $\tau = 0$.
According to equations (VI.4), (VI.5), and (VI.13),

$$A = \begin{bmatrix} -3 & 1 \\ -2 & 0 \end{bmatrix}, \qquad C(t) = \begin{bmatrix} -2/5e^{-t} & 0 \\ -4/5e^{-t} & 0 \end{bmatrix},$$

$$B = \begin{bmatrix} 2/5e^{-t} & 0 \\ -1/5e^{-t} & 0 \end{bmatrix}, \qquad b = \begin{bmatrix} 0 \\ 0 \end{bmatrix}, \tag{VI.29}$$

and the weighting-function matrix defined by equation (VI.16) is

$$\mathbf{W}(t-\theta) = \begin{bmatrix} 2e^{-2(t-\theta)} - e^{-(t-\theta)} & e^{-(t-\theta)} - e^{-2(t-\theta)} \\ 2e^{-2(t-\theta)} - 2e^{-(t-\theta)} & 2e^{-(t-\theta)} - e^{-2(t-\theta)} \end{bmatrix}. \tag{VI.30}$$

From equations (VI.29) and (VI.30),

$$\|\mathbf{W}(t-\theta)\|^2 = 10e^{-2(t-\theta)} - 18e^{-3(t-\theta)} + 10e^{-4(t-\theta)}, \tag{VI.31}$$

$$\|C(\alpha)\|^2 = 4/5\, e^{-2\alpha}, \tag{VI.32}$$

and

$$\|B(\theta)\|^2 = 1/5\, e^{-2\theta}. \tag{VI.33}$$

Since, in relation (VI.25), $\tau = 0$, and $\theta \geq 0$, it follows that

$$\int_\theta^t c_1 \|C(\alpha)\| d\alpha = \frac{2c_1}{\sqrt{5}} \left[e^{-\theta} - e^{-t} \right] \leq \frac{2c_1}{\sqrt{5}}. \tag{VI.34}$$

Substituting equations (VI.32), (VI.33), and (VI.34) into equation (VI.25), the relationship

$$\|\epsilon\| \leq c_1 M_y \exp\left\{\frac{2c_1}{\sqrt{5}}\right\} e^{-at} \int_0^t \frac{1}{\sqrt{5}} e^{(a-1)\theta} d\theta \tag{VI.35}$$

is formed. Relation (VI.35) becomes

$$\|\epsilon\| \leq \frac{c_1 M_y \exp\left\{\dfrac{2c_1}{\sqrt{5}}\right\}}{\sqrt{5}(a-1)} \{e^{-t} - e^{-at}\}, \tag{VI.36}$$

where

$$\left\|\mathbf{W}(t-\theta)\right\| \leq c_1 e^{-a(t-\theta)}. \tag{VI.37}$$

Now it can be shown that if $a = \frac{1}{2}$ and $c_1 = \sqrt{3}$, inequality (VI.37) is satisfied and equation (VI.36) becomes

$$\left\|\epsilon\right\| \leq \frac{2\sqrt{3} \exp\left\{\dfrac{2\sqrt{3}}{\sqrt{5}}\right\} M_y}{\sqrt{5}} \left\{e^{-t/2} - e^{-t}\right\}. \tag{VI.38}$$

From (VI.38) it is apparent that $\left\|\epsilon\right\|$ approaches zero as $t \to +\infty$. In addition it can be shown from this equation that

$$\max\left\|\epsilon\right\| = M_\epsilon \leq 1.81 M_y. \tag{VI.39}$$

The error bounds given in relations (VI.38) and (VI.39) are suitable for evaluating the approximation of equation (VI.27).

REFERENCES

1. Aseltine, J. A., "Transforms for Linear Time-Varying Systems," *Report No. 52-1*, University of California, Los Angeles, California, Department of Engineering, Jan., 1952.
2. Birkhoff, G., and S. MacLane, *A Survey of Modern Algebra*. New York: Macmillan, 1960.
3. Borskii, V., "On the Properties of Impulsive Response Functions of Systems with Variable Parameters," *Automation and Remote Control*, 20 (July, 1959), 822–830.
4. Cesari, L., *Asymptotic Behavior and Stability Problems in Ordinary Differential Equations*. Berlin: Springer-Verlag, 1959.
5. Coddington, E. A., and N. Levinson, *Theory of Ordinary Differential Equations*. New York: McGraw-Hill, 1955.
6. Cruz, J. B., "A Generalization of the Impulse Train Approximation for Time-Varying Linear System Synthesis in the Time Domain," *I.R.E. Transactions on Circuit Theory*, CT-6 (Dec., 1959), 393–394.
7. ———, "On the Realizability of Linear Differential Systems," *I.R.E. Transactions on Circuit Theory*, CT-7 (Sept., 1960), 347–348.
8. ———, and M. E. Van Valkenberg, "The Synthesis of Models for Time-Varying Linear Systems," in *Proceedings of the Symposium on Active Networks and Feedback Systems* (New York: Polytechnic Press of the Polytechnic Institute of Brooklyn, 1960), pp. 527–544.
9. Darlington, S., "An Introduction to Time-Variable Networks," in *Proceedings of Symposium on Circuit Analysis* (Urbana: University of Illinois, Department of Electrical Engineering, 1955), pp. 5-1–5-25.
10. ———, "Nonstationary Smoothing and Prediction Using Network Theory Concepts," *I.R.E. Transactions on Information Theory*, IT-5 (May, 1959), 1–11.
11. ———, "Time-Variable Transducers," in *Proceedings of the Symposium on Active Networks and Feedback Systems* (New York: Polytechnic Press of the Polytechnic Institute of Brooklyn, 1960), pp. 621–633.
12. Davenport, W. B., and W. L. Root, *An Introduction to the Theory of Random Signals and Noise*. New York: McGraw-Hill, 1958.
13. Gladkov, D. I., "On the Synthesis of Linear Automatic Control Systems," *Automation and Remote Control*, 22 (Oct., 1961), 263–270.
14. Ho, E. C., and H. Davis, "Generalized Operational Calculus for Time-Varying Networks," *Report No. 54-71*, University of California, Los Angeles, California, Department of Engineering, July, 1954.
15. Ince, E. L., *Ordinary Differential Equations*. New York: Dover, 1956.
16. Laning, J. H., and R. H. Battin, *Random Processes in Automatic Control*. New York: McGraw-Hill, 1956.
17. Leondes, C. T., ed., *Computer Control Systems Technology*. New York: McGraw-Hill, 1961.
18. Mal'chikov, S. V., "On the Synthesis of Linear Automatic Control Systems with Variable Parameters," *Automation and Remote Control*, 20 (Dec., 1959), 1543–1549.
19. Matyash, I., "Methods of Analog Computer Solution of Linear Differential Equations with Variable Coefficients," *Automation and Remote Control*, 20 (July, 1959), 813–821.
20. Miller, K. S., "Properties of Impulsive Responses and Green's Functions," *I.R.E. Transactions on Circuit Theory*, CT-2 (March, 1955), 26–33.

107

21. Siefert, W. W., and C. W. Steeg, Jr., ed., *Control Systems Engineering.* New York: McGraw-Hill, 1960.
22. Stear, E. B., and A. R. Stubberud, "Nonstationary Signal Flow Graph Theory," *Report No. 60–64,* University of California, Los Angeles, California, Department of Engineering, Nov., 1960.
23. ———, "Signal Flow Graph Theory for Linear Time-Variable Systems," *Transactions of the A.I.E.E. (Communications and Electronics),* 58 (Jan., 1962), 695–701.
24. Stubberud, A. R., "A Technique for the Synthesis of Linear Nonstationary Feedback Systems—Part I: The Approximation Problem," *I.E.E.E. Transactions on Applications and Industry,* 67 (July, 1963), 186–192.
25. ———, *ibid.,* "Part II: The Synthesis Problem," *I.E.E.E. Transactions on Applications and Industry,* 67 (July, 1963), 192–196.
26. Truxal, J. G., *Control Systems Synthesis.* New York: McGraw-Hill, 1955.
27. Zadeh, L. A., "A General Theory of Linear Signal Transmission Systems," *Journal of the Franklin Institute,* 253 (April, 1952), 293–312.
28. ———, "Circuit Analysis of Linear Varying-Parameter Networks," *Journal of Applied Physics,* 21 (Nov., 1950), 1171–1177.
29. ———, "Frequency Analysis of Variable Networks," *Proceedings of the I.R.E.,* 38 (March, 1950), 291–299.
30. ———, "The Determination of the Impulsive Response of Variable Networks," *Journal of Applied Physics,* 21 (July, 1950), 642–645.